BTEC First
Diploma in Applied Science

or

Science in Medicine

BTEC First
Diploma in Applied Science
Science in Medicine

Writing, editing and production

The **4science** team and associates
*www.***4science***.org.uk*

Images

Photos.com [Jupiter Images]
(unless otherwise stated)

Publisher

Edexcel
190 High Holborn
London WC1V 7BH
United Kingdom

Copyright

Safety

Teachers should make sure a risk assessment is carried out by a suitably qualified person before students undertake any practical activities.

Printed by Scotprint, Haddington
A catalogue record for this book is available from the British Library
ISBN 9 781846 901959

CONTENTS

- □ = worksheets
- □ = assignments
- □ = essential knowledge and data

INTRODUCTION

Welcome to the BTEC First Diploma in Applied Science: Science in Medicine book.

This book has worksheets, to help you learn relevant scientific topics, assignments, to show your progress in this unit and essential knowledge and data, to aid your understanding and help you complete your assignments.

Of course, books can't do everything for you. You still need to work hard to complete your coursework assignments and this will mean finding information from other sources.

During your course induction your tutor will provide you with information (sometimes contained in a student course handbook) about:

*   assignment work
*   assignment deadlines
*   building coursework portfolios
*   information gathering
*   how you will be assessed
*   practical work and health and safety in science laboratories.

More information and help is in the introduction pages of the Core Units book. There you will find a grid where you can track your progress for this and your other units.

The BTEC First Diploma in Applied Science is made up of six units and you must complete the Core Units:

Unit 1: Scientific Principles

Unit 2: Science and the World of Work

Unit 11: Science in Medicine will count as one of your other four specialist units.

BTEC courses are known as *work-related* and therefore the assignments you need to complete will have a work-related scenario e.g. working as a health professional who has to explain the action of a drug to fight infection.

The BTEC First Diploma course has both unit and course grades. You can achieve a pass, merit or distinction for this unit and for the overall course. If you are successful, the diploma you receive will contain both the unit and course grades. An example of this is below:

> The *individual units* have the following grades
> Pass for each of two units specified in the course programme
> Merit for each of four units specified in the course programme
> The *overall grade* for the BTEC First Diploma in Applied Science would be - Merit

The *Assessment Evidence Grid*, on the next page, shows:

*   the items that your portfolio must contain to achieve a pass grade
*   the additional work that you need to include to achieve a merit grade or distinction grade.

Assessment Evidence Grid: Unit 11: Science in Medicine

In order to pass this unit, the evidence that you present for assessment needs to demonstrate that you can meet all of the learning outcomes for the unit.

The criteria for a pass grade describe what you must do to pass this unit.

To achieve a pass grade the evidence must show that you are able to:	To achieve a merit grade the evidence must show that, in addition to the pass criteria, you are able to:	To achieve a distinction grade the evidence must show that, in addition to the pass and merit criteria, you are able to:
P1 identify and describe two biological and two physical procedures used to diagnose illness	M1 explain the scientific principles underlying the two biological and two physical procedures	D1 evaluate the advantages and disadvantages of using the two biological and two physical procedures
P2 identify the therapeutic drugs used to treat three given illnesses	M2 describe how the therapeutic drugs are used to treat these illnesses	D2 explain why the actions of therapeutic drugs are used to treat given illnesses
P3 describe two therapeutic techniques that are available to treat given examples of illnesses and conditions	M3 explain the functions of each of the techniques in given treatment processes	D3 evaluate the reasons why some individuals, religions and cultures choose not to take advantage of all types of available treatments
P4 describe how a new drug is identified and developed to production and marketing stages of development	M4 explain why very few of the compounds which start the process of development ever succeed through to become licensed drugs	D4 review the legal requirements for the introduction of a new drug into the UK market
P5 describe the factors affecting availability of drugs and treatments to patients.	M5 explain the general risks involved in all types of drug treatments.	D5 explain the reasons why decisions to give prescription drugs to some and not to others are always controversial.

WORKSHEETS

ASSIGNMENTS

BIOLOGICAL DIAGNOSIS

1: Causes of disease

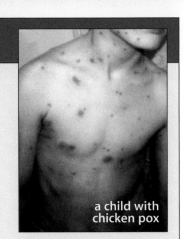

a child with chicken pox

Many things can make you feel ill or impair the normal way your body works.

- Some of them, like smoking or drug abuse, are self-inflicted.
- Others occur naturally.

Health has been defined by The World Health Organisation (WHO) as:

a complete state of physical, mental and social well-being, and not merely the absence of disease or infirmity.

With one or two other students, take five minutes to list diseases or medical conditions that you know about and make a second list of causes of ill-health.

Record your ideas here:

diseases or conditions affecting health	causes of ill-health

Compare your ideas with another group. Add their best (different) ones to your table (previous page).

Choose and list five different causes of ill-health below.

Add examples of diseases or conditions that each one causes.

cause of ill-health	examples of diseases or conditions

2: Diagnosing disease

As a pathologist or technician in a pathology laboratory, you would be interested in using biological methods to diagnose disease.

What does **diagnosing** a disease mean? Write your own definition here.

_____

_____

Use a library or the Internet to find other definitions. Write the best one here.

_____

_____

To make an accurate diagnosis, all necessary observations, measurements and tests must be carried out.

Pathologists and technicians work mainly in the laboratory, and give biological evidence that helps doctors decide on appropriate treatments. They use scientific techniques to:

- identify organisms causing disease
- inspect blood or other tissues for cell abnormalities
- carry out chemical analysis of blood, sputum (*phlegm*), urine or faeces
- conduct genetic investigations.

Identification of organisms causing disease

What kinds of organisms cause disease? *Germs* is a non-scientific word that describes all the microscopic organisms that cause disease. Use the wordsearch to find:

(a) the three main types of disease-causing microscopic organisms

(b) examples of diseases caused by each type.

- There are fifteen diseases in the wordsearch; see how many you can find on your own in five minutes.
- Add your findings to the table.
- Compare your answers with other students; add any missing examples.

```
A M S H S B A C T E R I A U
R U P M I N F L U E N Z A S
I N O R S L R U B E L L A I
N U L N E N P T E T A N U S
G C I H A N T H R A X N C T
W H O O P I N G C O U G H U
O I M V C E H R U V I S I O
R R R S Y P H I L I S M C P
M A L A R I A E O R I H K Y
P A R A S I T E S U I R E M
M E N I N G I T I S G I N P
T A U R A B I E S E C N P R
C A E E H T H R U S H N O O
M U M P S X W I R R G H X L
```

organisms			
diseases			

Symptoms

The first part of a diagnosis depends on the nature of the illness and the symptoms that the patient has. Discuss the next four questions with another student. Make notes of your ideas to answer them.

What symptoms do you have when you have a cold? Write some brief descriptions.

_____

_____

_____

_____

Some people think colds and 'flu are the same. Why do doctors need to be able to tell the difference?

_____

_____

What causes colds and 'flu to be different?

_____

_____

In 'flu, the doctor would look for:

•   general body aches (rather than problems being centred on the nose and head)
•   fever and raised temperature (unusual with a cold), flushed face
•   general lack of energy
•   possible dizziness or nausea
•   fever gives way to cold-like symptoms and a dry hacking cough
•   cough and lack of energy persist after other symptoms clear up
•   fever may come back.

What do you think? Is it easy to tell the difference between a cold and 'flu? Explain your answer.

_____

_____

_____

_____

3:   Diagnostic tests

Doctors often ask for tests to identify a disease that they can't conclusively recognise from its symptoms, or to confirm the identity of a disease and the organism that's causing it.

Have you ever had any medical tests? If so, write down what they were and what they were for (*you don't have to do this if you don't want to share the information*). Use the table on the next page. Talk to other students and choose one more example to add to the table. If you've never had any tests carried out, just use information from other students.

medical test (name and/or brief description)	reason for test	result - what information was gained?

4: Testing for organisms - Viruses

Bacteria in infected tissues (or other samples) can be found and identified with routine tests. Why are viruses more difficult to find and identify?

_____

_____

How could you show that a person was infected by the 'flu virus?

_____

_____

How can viral plaques be used to show how bad a viral infection is?

_____

_____

Virus culture needs large laboratories, expensive equipment and specially-trained technicians, molecular biologists and virologists. Results take time, so the normal way to detect viruses is to test for **antigens** in the structure of the virus or **antibodies** that a person makes in response to a virus infection.

Rapid 'flu tests, usable in a doctor's surgery, use the antigen-antibody reaction to give a result within 30 minutes or less.

Why is a speedy test important?

_____

_____

What other advantages do rapid 'flu tests have?

_____

_____

Rapid 'flu tests are about 70% reliable. They can give false results, both positive and negative.

Why is a *false negative* result more likely to be dangerous than a *false positive* result?

_____

_____

Scientists are investigating **nanotechnology techniques** (using minute molecular structures). These may be able to give an accurate diagnosis for a wide range of viruses from a single test within minutes of testing a sample.

What do you think is the biggest advantage of these new tests?

_____

_____

5: Testing for organisms - Bacteria

Classifying bacteria

Bacteria are very small. Their internal structure is limited and can't be seen using a light microscope. However, scientists in pathology laboratories still use light microscopes to look at the *shape* of bacteria. Shape gives a first clue to their identity.

Bacteria are usually colourless, so dyes or stains are used to make them visible. A sample is first spread thinly over the centre of a microscope slide, to separate the individual cells, before it is fixed and stained.

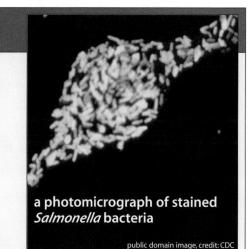

a photomicrograph of stained *Salmonella* bacteria

public domain image, credit: CDC

What is the size of a typical bacterium?

_____

What are the four main shapes to look out for? Complete the table, the first row has been done for you.

sketch of shape	description	biological name
◯	spherical	cocci (singular: coccus)

Scientists use various techniques and standard procedures to identify bacteria.

Read the following methods and ask your teacher which ones you should try.

Standard procedure: Preparation of a stained bacterial smear

Health and safety

A risk assessment must be carried out for all procedures before you start work. Biological material should be handled with caution. Wear a laboratory coat and report any spills. Follow your teacher's instructions for disposal of materials. Be careful - stains stain skin and clothing.

You will need

inoculating loop • distilled water in a wash bottle • safe source of bacteria (e.g. killed culture or yoghurt) • clean microscope slide • sticky label or fine permanent marker pen • Bunsen burner • beaker of disinfectant (e.g. *VirKon*) • clothes peg (spring type) • methylene blue stain and teat pipette or dropper • staining rack (if available) • sink or 250 cm^3 beaker • paper towel • optical microscope (minimum x400) •

You should know how to use a light (optical) microscope to carry out this procedure.

Method

1   Use a marker pen, or sticky label, and write your initials and the name of the sample being used on one end of a clean, dry microscope slide. Use the label to identify which side the sample is placed on.

2   If using colonies on a solid culture medium, add **one small** drop of distilled water to the centre of the slide (on the label side).

3   Have the source of the bacteria ready.

4   Hold the handle of the inoculating loop like a pen. Open the air hole of the Bunsen to get a roaring blue flame [CARE]. To avoid sputtering which could release microbes into the air:

   •   Place the handle end of the wire in the cool, light blue cone of the flame.

   •   Move the wire up slowly into the hottest part of the flame, just above the blue cone (hottest area).

   •   As the wire glows red hot, move it over the blue cone towards the loop so that every part of the wire has glowed red hot.

   •   Remove from the flame and allow to cool for a few seconds; do not put it down or wave it around.

5   Use the inoculating loop to transfer bacteria from the source to the slide:

   •   If using **colonies** on a solid culture medium, scrape a very small piece of a single colony onto the loop. Mix this into the drop of water on the slide

   •   If using a **liquid** (broth) culture, dip the loop into the culture and transfer a drop to the centre of the slide.

6   Spread thinly over the centre of the slide to cover an oval area up to 2 cm in length.

   *Note: The smear should be fairly transparent (**watery**). If it is opaque (**very cloudy**), dispose of the slide safely in the beaker of disinfectant. Repeat with a new slide, transferring less solid culture or diluting the broth with a small drop of water.*

7   Immediately after use, re-sterilise the wire loop to red hot (as in step 4). Follow the procedure to avoid sputtering. Allow to cool before putting down.

8   Close the air hole of the Bunsen burner to give a visible yellow flame.

9   Air-dry the slide (if necessary, the peg may be used to hold the slide in warm air, high above the Bunsen flame - do not overheat).

10   When completely dry, hold the slide with the peg at the label end. Pass the slide three times through the Bunsen flame. This **fixes** the bacteria ready for staining - it sticks their outer coat to the glass of the slide.

11   Over a sink or beaker, add one or two drops of methylene blue stain to the slide to cover the smear. The peg can be used to keep stain off your fingers, or use a staining rack if available. Leave for one minute.

12   Hold the slide at 45° and rinse the slide with tap or distilled water, into the sink or beaker, until the water runs clear.

13   Gently dry by **blotting** with a paper towel - do not wipe.

14   The stained smear should be visible to the naked eye. If not, the bacteria have been washed away. Repeat the procedure, but heat (step 9) a little more to fix effectively.

15   Use a microscope to view the stained bacteria. Work up through the powers from lowest power to highest power. Record your observations below.

16   If bacteria are not clearly visible, repeat the procedure, ensuring the slide does not get hot at the fixing (step 9) stage. Check by touching it gently against your hand: it should feel warm but not hot.

17   Place the used slide in the beaker of disinfectant.

18   Dispose of your source of bacteria safely, as instructed by your teacher.

Observations of bacteria

Describe and/or sketch the shapes of the bacteria on your slide.

Indicate which of the four basic types (by shape) are present.

Differential staining of bacteria

Bacteria have different outer layers. These make them react differently to stains. This is a way to distinguish them.

Dr Hans Christian Gram, pictured, devised a technique - called *The Gram Stain* - in 1884. Scientists in microbiology labs still use it today.

Using a single stain will reveal the shape of bacterial cells. Gram staining allows them to be distinguished depending on how well they retain the colour of a stain. Gram positive (G+) bacteria retain a purple colour from a first stain. Gram negative (G-) bacteria appear pink to red from a second stain.

public domain image

Standard procedure: Gram staining bacteria

Health and safety

A risk assessment must be carried out for all procedures before you start work. Biological material should be handled with caution. Wear a laboratory coat and report any spills. Follow your teacher's instructions for disposal of materials. Be careful - stains stain skin and clothing.

You will need

microscope slide with fixed bacterial smear • distilled water in a wash bottle (or tap) • 95% ethanol [HIGHLY FLAMMABLE] • crystal violet solution with teat pipette or dropper • clothes peg (spring type) • Lugol's iodine solution with teat pipette or dropper • safranin • staining rack (if available) • sink or 250 cm³ beaker • paper towel • optical microscope (minimum x400) • beaker of disinfectant for disposal of slides

Method

1   Over a sink or beaker, add two or three drops of crystal violet stain to the slide to cover the bacterial smear. The peg can be used to keep stain off your fingers, or use a staining rack if available. Leave for one minute.

2   Pour off stain.

3   Drip Lugol's iodine solution one drop at a time on to the slide held at 45⁰ over the sink or beaker, so it runs off the end. Continue until the iodine solution runs clear (usually about 30 seconds).

4   Over a sink or beaker, add one or two drops of Lugol's iodine solution to the slide to cover the smear. Leave for one minute.

5   Drip 95% ethanol one drop at a time on to the slide held at 45⁰ over the sink or beaker, so that it runs off the end. Continue until the washings are pale violet. Some bacteria lose their purple colour (decolourised) at this stage.

6   Rinse immediately with water.

7   Over a sink or beaker, add one or two drops of safranin stain to the slide to cover the smear. Leave for 30 seconds. Decolourised bacteria are stained red but purple bacteria keep their colour.

8   Rinse the slide with water, into the sink or beaker, until water runs clear.

9   Blot, do not wipe, the smear with paper towel to dry.

10   Use a microscope to view the stained bacteria. Work up through the powers from lowest power to highest power.

11   Record your observations. G+ bacteria will appear purple, G- appear pink or red.

12   If bacteria are not clearly visible, repeat the procedure.

13   Dispose of your slide safely, in the beaker of disinfectant.

Observations

List the shape/type of each type of bacterium you can see (**bacillus, coccus, spirillum** or **vibrio**).

Note the staining reaction:

* purple (colour retained) = G+
* red (purple colour lost) = G-

(Bacteria the same shape may stain differently.)

shape/type	Gram + or Gram –

Culturing bacteria

Bacteria can be cultured by giving them the conditions they need to grow.

This includes the correct nutrients, pH and temperature. In ideal conditions, growth is so rapid that visible colonies form within a day or two.

You can use standard procedures to investigate how you distinguish between colonies by the variations in their appearance. The agar plates should be left to cure, e.g. by leaving in the fridge overnight. This allows the surface to harden and makes streaking easier.

Standard procedure: Preparing nutrient agar plates

Health and safety

A risk assessment must be carried out for all procedures before you start work. Biological material should be handled with caution. Wear a laboratory coat and report any spills. Follow your teacher's instructions for disposal of materials. All micro-organisms in a sample multiply during incubation, including harmful ones. Therefore, after incubation samples MUST NOT be opened and must be disposed of safely [BIOHAZARD].

When you are not using a Bunsen burner, close its air hole so you can see a yellow flame. Keep it away from where you or others are working.

You will need

4 x sterile Petri dishes • 4 x bottles of liquid agar kept in a water bath at 45 - 50 °C • Bunsen burner • permanent marker pen • paper towels •

Method

1 Do not take the lids off the dishes. Turn the dishes over. Use a permanent marker pen to write your initials at the edge of the bottom of the dishes.

2 Collect a bottle of sterile liquid agar from the water bath and dry it with a paper towel.

3 Open the air hole of the Bunsen burner to turn it to a blue flame. Just above the blue flame is where the flame is hottest [CARE].

4 Loosen the cap of the bottle but don't open it.

5 If you're right handed, hold the bottle in your left hand and wrap the little finger of your right hand around the cap (if you're left handed use the opposite hand). Turn the bottle in your left hand to remove the cap. There is no need to keep the cap sterile because it is not being re-used. Put down the cap. Briefly pass the neck of the bottle through the hot part of the blue flame, still using your left hand.

6 With your right hand lift the lid of the Petri dish slightly open, just enough to pour the liquid agar into the dish. Quickly but carefully pour the contents of the bottle into the dish and close the lid immediately.

7 Discard the empty agar bottle.

8 Gently rotate the dish to spread the agar evenly over the base of the Petri dish.

Take care not to tip it, to reduce the chance of air bubbles.

9 Leave the Petri dish to cool and set.

Take care not to disturb the dish while the agar is setting.

10 Repeat the procedure for the other three dishes.

Standard procedure: Streaking cultures to produce colonies of bacteria

Health and safety

A risk assessment must be carried out for all procedures before you start work. Biological material should be handled with caution. Wear a laboratory coat and report any spills. Follow your teacher's instructions for disposal of materials.

All micro-organisms in a sample multiply during incubation, including harmful ones. Therefore, after incubation samples MUST NOT be opened and must be disposed of safely [BIOHAZARD].

When you are not using a Bunsen burner, close its air hole so you can see a yellow flame. Keep it away from where you or others are working.

You will need

4 x pre-prepared agar plates · bottle of sterile water · inoculation loop · broth culture of a bacterium · Bunsen burner · permanent marker pen · masking tape or biohazard tape ·

Method

1 Open the air hole of the Bunsen burner to turn it to a blue flame. This is when it's hottest [CARE]. The air around the blue flame is sterile so try to work close to it.

2 Loosen the lid of the bottle containing a bacterial culture, but do not open it.

3 Hold the top of the inoculating loop like a pen in your right hand (or left hand if you are left handed). Move the end of the wire loop into the blue cone of the flame and slowly draw the loop up through the hot part of the flame. The wire and loop should glow red hot. Hold the loop next to the flame for a few seconds for it to cool down.

4   Wrap your little finger (of the hand holding the inoculating loop) around the lid of the bottle. Turn the base of the bottle with your other hand and remove the lid. Keep the inoculating loop still and close to the flame but do not allow it to go into the flame.

5   Pass the neck of the bottle briefly back and forth once through the hot part of the blue flame [CARE].

6   Dip the wire loop into the culture and remove a small sample. Pass the neck of the bottle back and forth once through the blue part of the flame again. Put the lid back on the bottle and put it down on the bench.

7   Lift the lid of the Petri dish, keeping it above the agar plate Only lift the lid enough to put in the loop.

8   Move the loop forwards and backwards along the surface of the agar on one side of the plate to create an area containing a smeared sample (diagram 1).

9   Turn the Petri dish 90° anticlockwise. Look at diagram 2. Starting from point A, use the loop to make three streaks, spreading the sample to point B.

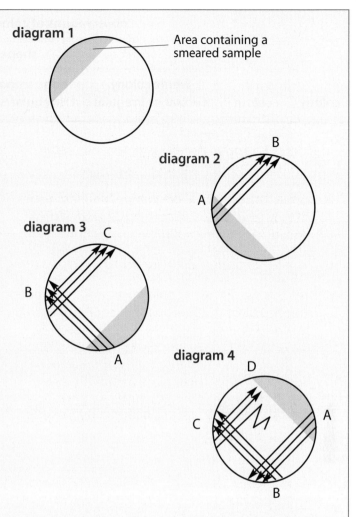

diagram 1 — Area containing a smeared sample

diagram 2

diagram 3

diagram 4

10   Make three streaks from point B to C (diagram 3) and three streaks from point C to point D, carrying the last streak into the centre of the agar (diagram 4). Remember to turn the plate through 90° each time. Replace the lid. This should result in some single colonies growing on the plate.

11   Flame and cool the loop as in step 3. Place the loop slowly into the flame, to avoid sputtering, then put it down.

12   Tape the lid to the base using four evenly-spaced short strips of sticky tape. DO NOT SEAL THE PLATE COMPLETELY. Turn the dish upside down.

13   Label around the edge of the base of the dish with: **the date** and **the name of the micro-organism** that you've streaked onto the plate.

14   Incubate the plate upside down at 25 °C for 48 hours.

Observations of bacterial colonies

Use

*   *Standard procedure: Preparing nutrient agar plates*, and

*   *Standard procedure: Streaking cultures to produce colonies of bacteria*

to grow visible colonies.

In the table (next page), record your observations for all the different types of colony.

Suggestions for descriptions are given, but use others if appropriate.

| | | observations of colony appearance | | | |
| colony | colour | shape | | | texture |
		whole colony circular or irregular	edge smooth or irregular/spiky	domed or flat	glossy, powdery, rough or waxy

How many different types of bacteria do you think you had in your culture plate?

_____

When you have colonies of different bacteria that share the same characteristics, you may use **differential plating** to distinguish them.

Do some research to find out about this (don't spend too long).

Describe how the standard procedure for preparing nutrient agar plates would be modified to do this.

_____

_____

_____

_____

Explain one way in which differential plating could distinguish two types of bacteria.

_____

_____

_____

5: Testing for organisms - Parasites

Malaria is the most common **protist** parasite of humans. It's thought to cause more than four million deaths every year.

Find out about the life cycle of the malarial parasite (*Plasmodium*).

Don't worry about the names of the different stages. Without going into any detail, explain how it is well adapted to spread from host to host.

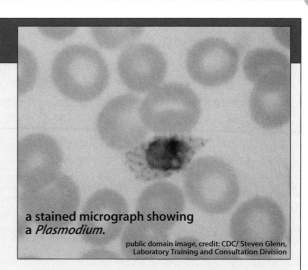

a stained micrograph showing a *Plasmodium*.

public domain image, credit: CDC/ Steven Glenn, Laboratory Training and Consultation Division

_____

_____

_____

_____

Malaria is characterised by recurrent fevers - the result of parasites and toxins released into the blood from red blood cells or liver cells.

Diagnosis is usually confirmed by microscopic inspection of blood smears. It's one example of how cell abnormalities are used to diagnose a disease.

6: Looking for cell abnormalities

If you know what normal tissues look like, you can spot the changes that take place in disease. Samples of tissues are removed for microscopic examination. Then the pathologist looks for the tell-tale signs of disease that will allow an accurate diagnosis.

What's the name of the process of taking a sample of cells from the body for microscopic examination?

_____

A variety of techniques are used to remove tissue samples (these are described in the *Essential knowledge and data* section at the end of this book).

How would a nurse, doctor or surgeon remove cells from the following.

The lining of the large intestine _____

_____

Bone marrow _____

_____

The cervix (for a cervical smear) _____

_____

A lump in a breast _____

_____

Blood sampling

Blood shows distinctive changes in a range of diseases. A few drops can be removed by using a sterile lancet (small sharp knife) to prick a finger (or the heel for a young child). This is enough to make thin smears on microscope slides.

If a drop of blood is placed on a slide, the cells are too close together to be easily distinguished when viewed with a light microscope. You can use standard procedures to make a blood smear and stain it to make cells and cell structures easier to see. This method spreads the cells apart, allowing red cells to be seen clearly.

Blood smears can be stained to make parasites, white blood cells and cancer cells easier to see.

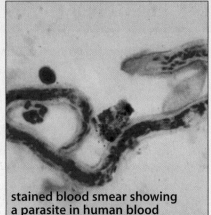

stained blood smear showing a parasite in human blood

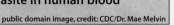
public domain image, credit: CDC/Dr. Mae Melvin

Inspecting blood smears for abnormalities

To spot abnormalities you must first know what is *normal*. In the space below, sketch diagrams and make notes to show what you would expect to find in a normal stained blood smear.

Standard procedure: Preparation of a blood smear

Health and safety

A risk assessment must be carried out for all procedures before you start work. Biological material should be handled with caution. Follow your teacher's instructions for disposal of materials.

You will need

safe source of mammalian blood [CARE: POSSIBLE BIOHAZARD] • capillary tube or disposable dropper • two clean microscope slides • sticky label or fine permanent marker pen • hair dryer or bench lamp • 95% ethanol [HIGHLY FLAMMABLE] with dropper or teat pipette (optional)

Method

1   Use the capillary tube or dropper to transfer a small drop of blood (about 2-3 mm across) to the end of a clean microscope slide. Touch the end of the capillary tube to the slide for a small drop of blood to form.

2   Use the second slide as a spreader.

- Support the end of the slide (farthest from the blood) between the thumb and forefinger of your left hand (or right hand if left-handed).

- Place an end of the spreader slide onto the centre of the other slide at an angle of 30-40° from the edge with the blood.

- Draw the spreader towards the blood until it just makes contact. The blood should spread to fill the angle between the two slides.

- Move the spreader towards the other end of the slide and tow the blood across in one slow smooth movement (see diagram).

- The blood should taper out before reaching the end of the slide, producing a feathered edge.

- There should be no ridges or holes.

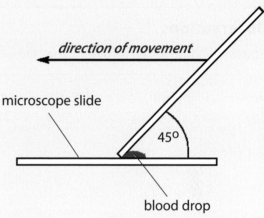

3   You should have a blood smear which gets thinner as it goes from the blood drop end to the other end of the slide. The centre of the smear will have cells spread out for easy viewing. If there was too little or too much blood, repeat with new slides using a larger or smaller drop as appropriate.

4   Place capillary tubes or droppers, spreaders and unwanted slides into the beaker of disinfectant.

5   Air dry the blood smear using a hair dryer or bench lamp. Do not overheat.

6   If the slide is not to be used straight away, it can be fixed in 95% ethanol for one minute. Do this by adding three or four drops to flood the smear with ethanol. Add additional ethanol if it evaporates too rapidly. Slides should be allowed to air dry before storage.

Standard procedure: Staining a blood smear using Giemsa's solution

Health and safety

A risk assessment must be carried out for all procedures before you start work. Biological material should be handled with caution. Follow your teacher's instructions for disposal of materials.

You will need

microscope slide with blood smear • Giemsa's solution [MAY BE HIGHLY FLAMMABLE, HARMFUL OR TOXIC DEPENDING ON FORMULATION] • coverslip • mounted needle • staining rack (if available) • sink or 250 cm^3 beaker • paper towel • optical microscope (minimum x200) • beaker of *VirKon* disinfectant •

You should know how to use a light (optical) microscope to carry out this procedure.

Giemsa's solution is a mixture of dyes which stains the nuclei and granules of white blood cells and other cells purple. Red blood cells appear pink.

Method

1   Place the blood smear slide on a staining rack or beaker.

2   Flood the smear with two or three drops of Giemsa's solution for 10-15 minutes. Add more stain if it evaporates.

3   Rinse the slide under a gently running tap, until the water runs clear.

4   Place a coverslip over the smear (protects the microscope high power objective). Blot away excess water with a paper towel.

5   Use a microscope to view the cells, working up through the powers from lowest power to highest power.

6   Record your observations below.

7   Dispose of your slide safely by placing in a beaker of *VirKon* disinfectant.

Observations

Describe and/or sketch cells from your slide.

Blood abnormalities

At the pathology laboratory, you are given blood samples from a number of patients. What would you look for, if you were given a blood smear from patients with these suspected conditions? Describe the features in the table.

suspected condition	abnormalities in blood to confirm diagnosis
anaemia	
sickle cell anaemia	

suspected condition	abnormalities in blood to confirm diagnosis
leukaemia	
malaria	

Do you think it's better to work *blind* when given a sample (in other words, no additional information) or should you know the rest of the patient's history?

Suggest one or two reasons to support each case.

It's better to test a sample without *a case history because ...*

_____

_____

_____

It's better to test a sample with *a case history because ...*

_____

_____

_____

7: Chemical analysis

Work with a partner to research for answers to these questions.

Diseases cause chemical changes in the body which can be detected in samples of blood, sputum (phlegm), urine or faeces. As a technician in a pathology laboratory, you could be sent any of these to test.

For each kind of sample, name or describe a test that could be carried out. Give a reason why the chemical change takes place in the sample when the patient has a particular illness.

Blood sample

Test for ...

_____

Reason ...

_____

_____

Sputum sample

Test for ...

_____

Reason ...

_____

_____

Urine sample

Test for ...

_____

Reason ...

_____

_____

Faeces (stool)

Test for ...

_____

Reason ...

_____

_____

ELISA

What does ELISA stand for?

_____

_____

Explain how an ELISA test can be used for pregnancy. You will need to do some research.

_____

_____

_____

_____

_____

_____

_____

_____

_____

_____

8: Genetic investigations

Carry out some research to complete the next two sections.

Work with one or two others to get the information you need. Write your answers in your own words.

List three inherited human conditions that affect health.

1 _____

2 _____

3 _____

Briefly describe what a **genetic counsellor** does.

_____

_____

_____

_____

_____

_____

Family history counselling and DNA analysis

Imagine you're a genetic counsellor.

What information would you give to a couple who are worried because the man's sister has just had a child with cystic fibrosis (CF)?

Write your answer in the form of a letter to the couple. Use the space on the next page.

Include the following:

•   Chances of them having a child with CF explained.

•   Tests available and how they work.

•   Options/choices they could take.

9: More about urine and blood tests

From acute appendicitis to Wilson's disease, the website *www.wrongdiagnosis.com* lists 54 types of disease that can be diagnosed using urine tests. For example, a simple colour change *dipstick* test can be used to detect glucose, protein or blood in the urine. These should normally be retained by the body, so their presence in the urine is a sign that something is wrong. Diabetes causes glucose to be lost in the urine.

The normal blood glucose level is 3.5 to 7.5 mmol/dm^3. In diabetes, the level rises above 9.0 mmol/dm^3. At this point the kidneys are no longer able to reabsorb all the glucose from the blood that they filter. So glucose is lost in the urine.

Why do blood glucose levels rise and fall through the course of the day?

_____

_____

Type 2 diabetes is often associated with obesity, onset of old age or lack of exercise. It's sometimes called insulin resistant diabetes. Insulin is produced, but the body does not respond fully to it. If a urine glucose test is positive and type 2 diabetes is suspected, a glucose tolerance test may be carried out.

Testing for glucose in urine and blood plasma

Your task is to use standard procedures to carry out glucose tests on simulated urine and blood plasma samples. You will be given:

- simulated urine samples from patients A, B and C

- simulated plasma samples from patients A and B, taken immediately before drinking glucose and two hours later.

Originally, doctors had to test urine samples by tasting them to see if they were sweet. Then urine had to be boiled with Fehling's solution - which is similar to Benedict's reagent - to get a brick-red precipitate.

Nowadays you can use a simple test strip for glucose. This contains an enzyme which specifically causes a reaction involving glucose to give a colour change.

Standard procedure: Testing for glucose in urine

Health and safety

A risk assessment must be carried out for all procedures before you start.
Wear protective clothing and eye protection.

You will need

simulated urine samples (special health and safety measures would be required for real body fluids) • test tubes • test tube rack • permanent marker • glucose test strips • diagnostic colour graph • teat pipettes

Method

1   Label a test tube for each sample to be tested.

2   Use a clean teat pipette to transfer about 2 cm^3 of *urine* sample to a labelled test tube.

3   Dip a test strip into the sample and allow it to develop (change colour if glucose is present).

4   Compare the colour of the test strip with the colour graph and record the glucose range of the sample.

5   Repeat for any further samples.

Results

Record your results in the table.

sample	glucose range

Recommendations

Which samples suggest possible diabetes and further testing using a glucose tolerance test?

_____

Testing for glucose in blood plasma

You can find glucose concentration in blood plasma samples by timing how long it takes for the glucose to decolourise potassium manganate solution. Glucose reduces purple-pink manganate ions to colourless manganese ions and water. The higher the glucose concentration, the faster the reaction.

You will need to make your own calibration graph. You …

- time how long it takes known glucose solutions to decolourise the manganate
- plot a graph of *time* against *glucose concentration* (calibration graph)
- time how long it takes a plasma sample to decolourise the manganate
- read the glucose concentration of the plasma off the calibration graph.

Standard procedure: Analysing plasma samples for glucose tolerance testing

Health and safety

A risk assessment must be carried out for all procedures before you start.
Wear protective clothing and eye protection.

You will need

Eye protection • stopclock/timer • glass stirring rod • boiling tube and rack • 10 cm^3 measuring cylinders • dropping pipettes or syringes • glucose solutions (2%, 4%, 6%, 8%, 10%, 12%) • simulated blood plasma samples A0, A2, B0 and B2 (special health and safety measures would be required for real body fluids) • 1 mol/dm^3 sulfuric acid [IRRITANT] • potassium manganate solution (0.4 g/dm^3) [LOW HAZARD]

Method

1   Measure 10 cm^3 of 2% glucose solution into the boiling tube.

2   Measure 5 cm^3 of 1 mol/dm^3 sulfuric acid and add to the boiling tube from 1.

3   Zero the stopclock.

4   Use a dropping pipette to take 2 cm^3 potassium manganate solution from a measuring cylinder (or use a syringe).

5   Add the potassium manganate to the boiling tube, simultaneously starting the stopclock.

6   Stir the contents of the boiling tube with a stirring rod and stop the clock as soon as the solution appears colourless.

7   Record the time taken to go colourless in the table below.

8   Thoroughly wash the boiling tube and dropping pipettes or syringes.

9   Repeat steps 2-8 for the remaining glucose solutions.

10   Collect any class results and calculate the mean times to go colourless for each glucose solution.

11   Plot a graph of *mean time to go colourless* against *concentration of glucose*. (Grid provided next page). This is your calibration graph.

12   Repeat steps 1-8, using blood plasma samples instead of glucose solutions.

   •   A0 represents a blood plasma sample taken from patient A immediately before drinking a glucose solution.

   •   A2 represents a sample taken two hours later.

   •   B0 and B2 are similar samples taken from patient B.

13   Use the calibration graph to estimate the glucose concentrations of your blood plasma samples and record them below.

14   Collect any class results and calculate the average glucose concentrations of the blood plasma samples.

Results

glucose concentration / %	2	4	6	8	10	12
time to go colourless / s						
class mean time / s						

patient	sample of blood plasma	time to go colourless / s	glucose concentration / %	class mean glucose concentration / %
A	A0 (taken at start)			
	A2 (taken two hours later)			
B	B0 (taken at start)			
	B2 (taken two hours later)			

Conclusions

Which patient (A or B) is most likely to be suffering form diabetes? Explain your answer.

Note: The glucose concentrations are higher than those actually found in the blood, but the pattern of change is the same as in real cases.

_____

_____

_____

_____

_____

_____

_____

_____

_____

_____

_____

_____

_____

_____

Did any of your results vary from the class mean values? If so, state which samples were different:

_____

_____

_____

If yes, suggest possible reasons.

_____

_____

_____

_____

_____

_____

10: More about cytology

If you're working in a pathology laboratory, you may need to investigate cell appearance for abnormalities found in disease. You may need to be able to obtain tissue samples, then prepare and inspect them using a microscope.

Your task is to:

- use standard procedures to obtain a cheek cell sample
- stain the cheek sample using the *Pap* staining technique
- inspect the cheek sample using a light microscope.

Cheek cells and *Pap* staining

Cheek cells are a good example of an epithelial (lining) tissue which is constantly wearing away and being replaced. Loose cells are easy to obtain for staining.

The *Pap* or Papanicolaou staining technique is named after its inventor, who is considered to be the *father of cytopathology.* It's a differential stain: a mixture of dyes to stain dissimilar cells and cell structures so they show up in contrasting colours. This makes abnormal cells, such as cancer cells, with large nuclei easier to detect.

The stain is very reliable and can be used on a wide variety of smears of bodily samples, such as sputum, urine and fine-needle biopsy materials.

When used in cervical cancer screening, the entire procedure of obtaining and staining a smear is called a *Pap smear*.

Read and use the following standard procedures to obtain, stain and view a cheek cell sample.

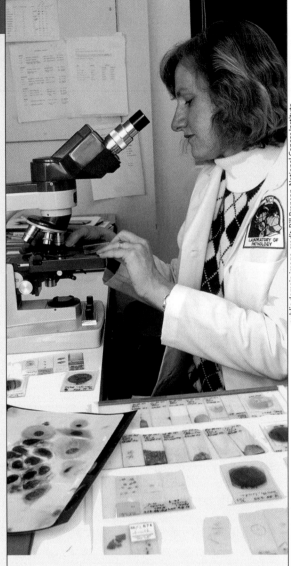

public domain image, credit: Bill Branson, National Cancer Institute

a scientist examining Pap smears under the microscope

Standard procedure: Obtaining a cheek cell sample

Health and safety

A risk assessment must be carried out for all procedures before you start. Biological material, especially if of human origin, should be handled with caution. Under no circumstance should you handle any swabs taken or used by other students. Make sure you dispose of your own swab as directed by your teacher.

You will need

sterile mouth swab or cotton bud (sealed) • disinfectant in a beaker • sterile Petri dish or other container

Method

1   Use a swab or cotton bud from a newly opened packet.

2   Wipe over the inside of **one** cheek and along the lower outer surface of the gum.

3   If not used immediately, place in suitable sterile container such as a Petri dish.

4   Once used, place the swab in a beaker of disinfectant for disposal.

Standard procedure: Pap staining a cheek cell sample

Health and safety

A risk assessment must be carried out for all procedures before you start. Biological material, especially if of human origin, should be handled with caution. Under no circumstance should you handle any swabs taken or used by other students. Make sure you dispose of your own swab as directed by your teacher.

You will need

cheek cell sample on mouth swab or cotton bud (sealed) • microscope slides • distilled water • tap water • orange G solution (OG6) [HAZARDOUS, HANDLE WITH CARE] • EA36 [HAZARDOUS, HANDLE WITH CARE] • 95%, 80% and 70% ethanol [HIGHLY FLAMMABLE] • dimethyl benzene (xylene) [HARMFUL, HIGHLY FLAMMABLE] • DPX [HARMFUL] • Harris's haemotoxylin [HARMFUL] • propan-2-ol (isopropyl alcohol) [HIGHLY FLAMMABLE, IRRITANT] • disinfectant in a beaker • hydrochloric acid 0.5% [CORROSIVE] • teat pipettes

Method

1   Use the mouth swab or cotton bud to smear a sample of cheek cells over the centre of a clean microscope slide.

2   Place the used swab or cotton bud immediately into disinfectant in a suitable container.

3   Pipette a small amount of fixative, isopropyl alcohol, onto the smear on the slide. Leave for five minutes. This kills and preserves the cells.

4   Shake off the fixative and flood the smear with four or five drops of 95% ethanol for one minute.

5   Shake off the ethanol and flood the smear with 80% ethanol for one minute.

6   Shake off the ethanol and flood the smear with 70% ethanol for one minute.

7   Shake off the ethanol and flood the smear with distilled water for one minute.

8   Shake off the water and flood the smear with Harris's haematoxylin stain for five minutes.

9   Rinse the slide in very gently running tap water for two minutes.

10   Flood the slide with a few drops of 0.5% hydrochloric acid for one minute.

11   Shake off the acid and repeat with fresh acid.

12   Use a microscope to check that only the nuclei of the cells are stained. If necessary, rinse with more acid and check again.

13   Rinse the slide in very gently running tap water for three to five minutes until the sample turns blue.

14   Shake off the water and flood the smear with Harris's haematoxylin stain for five minutes.

15   Shake off the ethanol and flood the smear with 70% ethanol for one minute

16   Shake off the ethanol and flood the smear with 95% ethanol for one minute.

17   Add a few drops of orange G stain (OG6) for two minutes.

18   Shake off the stain and flood the smear with 95% ethanol for one minute.

19   Repeat with further 95% ethanol twice more.

20   Either add a coverslip to make a temporary mount and view using a microscope or:

21   Flood the slide with a few drops of xylene for one minute.

22   Mount in DPX: place a drop of DPX over the smear. Gently drop a coverslip over the DPX at an angle, so it squeezes out the air as it falls. View using a microscope. Work up through the objective powers.

Observations

Look for differential staining: how are different structures stained in different ways?

You may wish to make labelled sketches of what you can see.

PHYSICAL DIAGNOSIS

1: Vital signs

Work with one or two other students to answer the problems which follow. Use the *Essential knowledge and data* section of this book or other sources of information to help you.

If you are unwell and see the doctor or are in hospital, certain measurements are usually taken. These will give clues about your health and help diagnosis. After treatment has started, they will indicate whether you're getting better.

List the four vital signs that are usually monitored when you're ill.

_____

_____

_____

_____

These measurements are quick and easy to take in a hospital, doctor's surgery, at home or at the site of a medical emergency. They give useful information about your general health and give clues to help diagnose illnesses. Changes in vital signs indicate whether you are getting better or if your illness is getting worse.

2: Body temperature

The norm for body temperature used to be given as 37.0 °C. Explain what is meant by *norm*.

_____

_____

Human body temperature through the day

A study was carried out to investigate human body temperature over the course of 24 hours. Use the results shown in the table to plot a graph of body temperature against time of day. Use the grid provided.

time of day	body temperature / °C
0700	36.5
0900	36.7
1100	37.3
1300	37.4
1500	37.4
1700	37.5
1900	37.4
2100	37.2
2300	37.0
0100	36.3
0300	36.2
0500	36.3

What do the results tell you about human body temperature?

_____

_____

Suggest reasons for the pattern shown on the graph.

_____

_____

_____

_____

_____

What other information do you think would have been useful?

_____

_____

_____

_____

_____

What does the NHS Direct website give as the norm for body temperature?

_____

Suggest possible reasons why the results from the study above do not lie within this range.

_____

_____

_____

_____

Fevers

You suffer from a fever when your body temperature becomes too high.

At what temperature would you be diagnosed as having a fever?

_____

Fever wordsearch

Highlight the words in the wordsearch which are common causes of fever (right or down).

List your causes of fevers (you should have ten).

1 _____

2 _____

3 _____

4 _____

5 _____

6 _____

7 _____

8 _____

9 _____

10 _____

```
L E H E A R T A T T A C K W U M
O A W I A A A I U M N I R H S B
H R E E I M O A I E T S I O I C
G I N F L U E N Z A I I I O C R
E N E O A M T O K S B T Z P H S
M F F E N P A N E L I L S I I N
E E C Z H S N O O E O S E N C C
T C O N N P S N L S T A T G K H
N T C S I I I O F M I F I C E O
K I D N E Y I N F E C T I O N S
T O N S I L L I T I S N Z U P M
N N X O A I N P X K L S H G O H
S S E N N N O I I K A N X H X N
G U I N R A M I I T H C T A T U
I K A S A O I C A A M I N L X E
K I P E P G U C E M K I N O H E
```

Heat stroke

Explain the difference between heat stroke and fever.

_____

_____

Hypothermia

Hypothermia is caused by getting too cold. Why is it a good idea to wear a hat in very cold surroundings?

_____

_____

Explain how you could get hypothermia in mild weather if you got wet, especially if it was windy.

_____

_____

Critical temperatures

Draw lines to match each statement to the correct temperature. *Note: Death connects to two temperatures.*

condition	temperature / °C
high fever, very red and severe sweating	24-27
normal	28-31
shivering increases, skin becomes blue	32-35
death	36-36.8
confusion leading to coma	38
fever	39
	44

Measuring body temperature

Body temperature used to be measured using mercury-in-glass clinical thermometers.

How is a clinical thermometer different from a normal laboratory thermometer? Describe as many differences as you can.

_____

_____

_____

_____

What other methods are available for measuring body temperature?

_____

_____

_____

Suggest reasons why mercury-in-glass thermometers are being phased out.

_____

_____

_____

_____

_____

What is the more usual modern method for measuring body temperature?

_____

_____

Give two advantages of using this method.

_____

_____

Where in the body can temperature be measured? List the different places that are normally used.

_____

_____

Choose two of the places in the body that will show different results. Explain why different temperature readings will be obtained.

_____

_____

An investigation of body temperature

Health and safety

A risk assessment must be carried out before starting work. Avoid using mercury-in-glass thermometers. Thermometers or probes used to measure oral temperatures must be sterilised between users. Replaceable probe covers should be used for ear thermometers.

You will need

two or three different devices for measuring body temperature • any consumable materials for their use • probes with data logging equipment, if possible

Introduction

Your task is to investigate factors which affect the measurement of human body temperature. You should work with two or three other students to design and carry out investigations to compare the effects of temperature measurements:

• using two different temperature measuring devices

• for males and females

• for two different places in the body

• for different times of day .

Your teacher will give you further guidelines, including the timescale for your investigation and standard procedures for the devices which you use. Try to organise class results so that they can be combined for analysis.

Method

1 Work with your group to design your investigation. You will need information from your teacher on:

   • timescale - how much class time will you have and what are the deadlines?

   • apparatus and procedures - what methods will you use to measure body temperature?

   Keep a record of your work.

2 Hold a class discussion to exchange ideas and co-operate for the collection of compatible results.

3 Adopt and adapt the best methods for your final design. Include a diary of events and targets to meet. Keep these in a separate portfolio of your work.

4 Check your plans with your teacher.

5 Carry out your investigation, write up your methods and record your results.

6 Where appropriate, share results with other groups.

7 Analyse the results and form conclusions.

8 Use a suitable format to present your results and conclusions to the rest of the class.

   You should consider:

   • What do the results show - what patterns or connections are there?

   • How will you explain your results?

     - What caused the patterns or connections?

     - Are the causes due to biological factors, apparatus used or the way the investigation was carried out?

   • How reliable are the results? Would you expect to get the same results if you carried out the investigation again?

   • How might you improve the investigation?

   • What firm, valid conclusions can you draw from your results?

9 After a class discussion, use your own words to summarise the results and conclusions on the next page.

Results and conclusions

3: Blood pressure

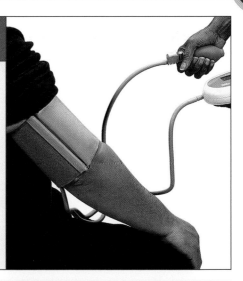

Blood pressure: the pressure generated by the circulating blood pressing against the artery walls.

Blood pressure is measured using a **sphygmomanometer**. Use the following standard procedure, or another provided by your teacher, to investigate the measurement of blood pressure.

Traditionally the non-SI units millimetres of mercury (mmHg) have been used to measure blood pressure, with systolic pressure separated from diastolic pressure by a forward slash, e.g. 120/80. This is stated as *120 over 80*.

Standard procedure: Measuring blood pressure

Health and safety

You must conduct a risk assessment and check it with your teacher before carrying out this procedure.

You will need

- sphygmomanometer

Method

Follow the instructions provided with the apparatus. Different types tend to give slightly different readings. So, it's important to use the same instrument each time, if you want to make comparisons.

Many factors may affect blood pressure, so it's important to exclude those which have a significant effect, notably:

- Don't drink coffee, smoke cigarettes or take other drugs for at least 30 minutes before testing.
- Empty your bladder before testing (a full bladder affects blood pressure).
- If possible avoid Mondays (blood pressure tends to peak on Mondays).

If an arm cuff is to be used, wear short sleeves or sleeves that can be loosely rolled up.

Basic blood pressure at rest

Before taking readings sit for five minutes with back supported and feet flat on the ground with the arm on a table at the level of the heart.

Blood pressure following exercise

Take readings sitting as above, but as soon as possible.

An automatic electronic sphygmomanometer

1   Determine if it is a wrist or arm type. Place the cuff in the correct position and fasten securely.

2   For a wrist type it is important to maintain the wrist at the level of the heart.

3   Press the *on* button. The cuff will automatically inflate and then slowly deflate.

4   Record the systolic and diastolic pressures shown on the digital display, together with heart rate.

5   Leave for two minutes and then repeat. If values are not consistent, a third reading may be necessary. Reject any inconsistent reading.

If values vary, it may be necessary to repeat the procedure later. Don't keep taking readings: allow the participant to rest.

Considerable caution is needed when interpreting results. Many factors can affect the results. Use your own words to summarise the results and conclusions on the next page.

Results and conclusions

High blood pressure

What is considered to be a *healthy norm* for blood pressure?

_____

_____

What is considered to be a *high blood pressure* (**hypertension**)?

_____

_____

Why is blood pressure normally measured several times, over a period of time, before high blood pressure is diagnosed?

_____

_____

_____

_____

List five factors which increase the risk of developing high blood pressure.

1 _____

2 _____

3 _____

4 _____

5 _____

Why is having high blood pressure significant?

_____

_____

_____

_____

4: Body imaging methods

Observing your appearance and measuring vital signs can help doctors decide what's wrong with you.

Sometimes they need information about what's happening inside the body, out of sight.

Give four medical imaging methods used to diagnose and observe disease in areas which are not normally visible.

1 _____

2 _____

3 _____

4 _____

Image released under terms of GNU Free Documentation License

It's likely that you've been investigated using body imaging techniques - probably before you were even born!

What medical imaging technique is used to investigate the development of the fetus inside the womb?

_____

_____

Name three other *non-invasive* imaging techniques used to look inside the body.

1 _____

2 _____

3 _____

Name another technique that is *minimally invasive* (in other words, it doesn't require major surgery to open up the body).

_____

_____

Why do doctors and surgeons need to look inside the body?

_____

_____

_____

_____

X-ray wordsearch

In the wordsearch, find nine disorders that can be found using X-rays. Write them here:

1 _____

2 _____

3 _____

4 _____

5 _____

6 _____

7 _____

8 _____

9 _____

```
O A R T H R I T I S J U A E D
D R I U L E O O T O C D I T I
C E E B R O S J S R R R I I S
B D S E E D A N A O O C H L L
R C R R H R T R A S U A L U O
E D F C R T C C E T T S T N C
A O R U C O E R B E R B B G A
S W A L L O W E D O B J E C T
T I C O C T R L R P S I U A E
T R T S I H T R E O T C R N D
U O U I E D T U C R O T T C J
M T R S E E S U U O A E N E O
O D E T U C A T N S D N T R I
U A S G U A L W R I T W O E N
R O R B P Y T A O S A A S O T
```

Helping X-rays

As a radiographer, you might ask for a patient to be given a **barium meal** or to have **opaque dye** injected into their blood.

Explain why radiographers use these techniques and what they would be looking for.

• Why put opaque materials into the gut or blood?

_____

_____

_____

• What might be seen in the gut?

_____

_____

• What might be seen in the blood vessels?

_____

_____

Comparing imaging techniques

Choose four medical imaging techniques. For each one, briefly describe:

• how it works

• what it can be used for

• one advantage

• one disadvantage.

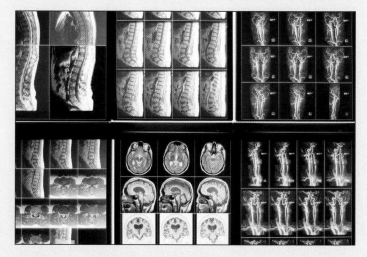

imaging technique 1:

how it works:	uses:	advantage:	disadvantage:

imaging technique 2:

how it works:	uses:	advantage:	disadvantage:

imaging technique 3:

how it works:	uses:	advantage:	disadvantage:

imaging technique 4:

how it works:	uses:	advantage:	disadvantage:

1: Therapeutic drugs

There are many drugs that can be used to treat conditions or illnesses.

- Some are considered relatively safe to use and can be bought **over the counter**.
- Other therapeutic drugs are available **on prescription**.

Explain these two terms:

over the counter

_____

_____

on prescription

_____

_____

Name two **over the counter** drugs and two **prescription drugs** that you, a friend or a relative has used. Describe what it was used for.

over the counter drugs	purpose/use
1	
2	

prescription drugs	purpose/use
1	
2	

2: How drugs are administered

To work, drugs have to reach their *site of action* in the body.

The formulation of a drug into a medicine means it's made up in a certain way, so the correct amount of drug can get to where it needs to be.

Usually, the blood is used to transport drugs to the disease-causing organisms or affected tissues.

Name and describe three methods for administering drugs so they reach the bloodstream.

1 _____

_____

2 _____

_____

3 _____

_____

Give an example of a drug treatment where the drug does not need to enter the bloodstream.

_____

_____

If you wanted a drug to take action as quickly as possible, what could you do? Give an example.

_____

_____

Example: _____

_____

If you wanted small amounts of a drug to be released into the blood at regular intervals from a single dose, what could you do? Give an example.

_____

_____

Example: _____

_____

3: Medicines

Drugs are not just sold as the pure chemical. They need to be in a form that can be taken up in the right place in the body.

Drug companies also need to make a profit - they are in competition with each other.

Your task is to investigate the factors which affect how drugs are formulated, priced and marketed.

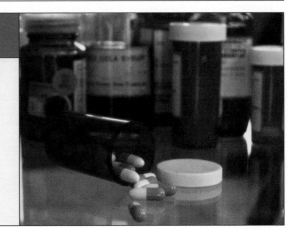

Investigating *over the counter* medicines

Work with one or two other students on this investigation.

- Choose one *over the counter* drug to investigate. It might be an antihistamine, a cough medicine, a pain killer, a treatment for indigestion or diarrhoea - any medicine that can be bought from the supermarket or pharmacy shelves without a prescription.

- Your teacher may allocate examples to different groups. They will set your deadline for this work.

> **Note:** Do not bring any medicines to school (unless you have an agreed official arrangement with your school). You may bring packaging and information leaflets.

Record the name of your chosen drug. _____

If this is a brand name, give the name of the therapeutic drug(s) it contains.

_____

Cost (give the price and a description of the quantity).

_____

_____

Read the information provided with your medicine.

There will normally be information on the packet and an explanatory leaflet.

Name the manufacturer.

_____

Describe its use (what is the medicine used to treat?).

_____

_____

_____

_____

Describe the formulation of the medicine (how is it administered - oral tablet, topical ointment etc?).

_____

State the dosage. You should indicate numbers of tablets or volumes of liquids etc. State the quantity of active drug that is given in one dose (e.g. mg of chemical) and how often it should be taken.

_____

Calculate the cost per dose. Show your working.

_____

_____

_____

_____

List the ingredients and, where you can, explain why they are in the medicine (staple a separate table to this page if you need more space).

ingredient	purpose

Describe any reasons why some people should not take the medicine (state none, if not relevant).

_____

_____

Give two examples of reasons why someone should tell their doctor if they are taking the medicine (state none, if not relevant).

1 _____

_____

2 _____

_____

Describe any possible side effects (state none, if not relevant).

_____

_____

_____

_____

Comment on the packaging of your medicine. How is it different from what you would expect if it were the cheapest possible, basic package?

_____

_____

_____

_____

Suggest some reasons why the package is not the simplest and cheapest possible.

_____

_____

_____

_____

Comparison with another medicine

You've probably heard of *Viagra*. But did you know it's a *branded medicine*? This is the brand name given by the drug company Pfizer to the *generic medicine* sildenafil.

Use your own words to describe the difference between a branded medicine and a generic medicine.

_____

_____

_____

_____

Is the medicine branded or generic?

_____

Now choose anther over the counter medicine to compare with your original choice.

*   If yours is a branded medicine, try to find a generic partner, or vice versa.

*   If this is not possible, try to find a medicine containing the same active chemical (drug).

*   If you can't do this either, choose a medicine which is used to treat the same condition.

Name of medicines for comparison _____

Describe how the medicines are similar (use another sheet of paper if you need more space).

_____

_____

_____

_____

_____

_____

_____

Describe how the medicines are different (use another sheet of paper if you need more space).

Try to explain any differences you have observed (use another sheet of paper if you need more space).

4: Drugs crossword

What different kinds of drugs are there and how do they work? Use the *Essential knowledge and data* section of this book and/or other sources to help you solve this crossword. This will help you to prepare for your first assessed assignment.

Across

1 _____ blockers help to prevent angina by slowing and reducing the force of heart beats.

5 Statins can be used to lower the levels of _____ in the blood.

7 Temazepam can be used to treat sleeplessness, it is an example of a _____.

9 Penicillin is a kind of _____.

11 Beta blockers can help to treat angina by blocking the action of the hormone _____.

12 Histamine is produced when you come in contact with something that you are _____ to.

14 The way that a drug is made up ready for use is called its _____.

15 Some drugs in liquid form may be given by an _____ injection into a vein.

16 The _____ is the organ in the body that breaks down drugs.

17 _____ can be used as an analgesic and an anti-inflammatory.

22 _____ is an example of a non-drowsy antihistamine.

23 An _____ can be used for topical administration of a drug.

24 _____ block the transmission of pain signals in the brain.

25 An opioid such as _____ can be used to ease severe pain.

26 The second S in SSRI stands for _____.

Down

2 _____ inhibitors are powerful vasodilators used to lower blood pressure and treat angina.

3 MRSA refers to Staphylococcus aureus that is resistant to _____.

4 Amphetamines increase wakefulness by stimulating _____ cells to release noradrenaline.

6 Insulin is used to treat _____.

8 Some antidepressants work by increasing the amount of chemical _____ at nerve endings in the brain.

10 _____ drugs can be used to kill cancer cells.

12 Aspirin can act as an _____ (pain killer) or an anti-pyretic.

13 Coffee and tea act as a stimulants because they contain _____.

18 Tamoxifen opposes the effects of the hormone _____, which stimulates some breast cancers.

19 Certain stimulants can be used to help newborn babies with _____ difficulties.

20 Antibiotics can be used to kill _____.

21 Because it's a _____ which would be digested if taken in tablet form, insulin is usually injected.

THERAPEUTIC TECHNIQUES

1: Using therapeutic techniques

Try this on your own. Then compare your answers with other students to check and fill in gaps.

There are many conditions or illnesses that aren't treated by drugs or by drugs alone.

Try to fill in the gaps in this table to give matching examples of ill health or types of treatment techniques.

illlness/condition	treatment technique
	blood transfusion
appendicitis	
short sightedness	
	acupuncture
	vaccination
kidney failure	
arthritis of the hip joint	
	low cholesterol diet
cancer	1 2
muscle strain or back injury	1 2 3

2: Investigating a therapeutic technique

Your task is to do some initial research to help you complete your first assessed assignment.

- Your teacher will give you further guidance.
- You may be given or asked to choose a technique to investigate.
- You may be asked to work alone or as part of a small group.
- You will need to do some research to obtain the necessary information.
- Your final report will be used by other students.
- This activity is in three parts: *research, reporting* and *reviewing*.

Part 1: Research

For your selected technique ...

Name the technique. _____

Research and make notes on the following (use another sheet of paper if you need more space).

What the technique is used for ...

_____
_____
_____
_____
_____
_____

How the technique works (you may want to make diagrams) ...

_____
_____
_____
_____
_____
_____
_____
_____
_____
_____
_____
_____
_____
_____
_____
_____
_____
_____

Part 2: Reporting

Report your findings on one side of A4. Use a word processor, if possible.

- Include what you consider to be the most important information.

- Be concise - use notes rather than sentences.

- Be clear - explain any technical terms.

- Display your report for other students to see (all the reports should remain available for use).

Part 3: Reviewing therapeutic techniques

Look at the other reports. Make a list of the techniques covered by them.

_____

_____

_____

_____

_____

_____

_____

_____

_____

_____

_____

_____

You may wish to use information in the reports to help you complete your first assignment.

3:   Treatment for all?

Not all modern medical practice is acceptable to everyone. Cultural, religious or personal beliefs affect people's choices of potential treatments for themselves and their children. Using Jehovah's Witnesses or pro-life groups as an example, briefly explain why some people choose not to take advantage of all types of available treatments ...

_____

_____

_____

_____

_____

_____

ASSIGNMENT – DIAGNOSING AND TREATING ILLNESS

Introduction

You will be given further guidance by your teacher, including an assignment frontsheet on which you should write your deadline. You will be expected to sign the front sheet to indicate that your assessed work is all your own work.

This is a long assignment with a number of associated tasks. Be careful to plan your work so that you can meet the deadline comfortably. Remember that you may need to revisit some work if you do not meet the criteria the first time. Be sure to ask whenever you are unsure about something.

Scenario

Northport is a city on the coast. It has a large population of retired people. A medical practitioner is working in the Accident and Emergency Department of the Northport District General Hospital.

On one particular day, a number of patients came through the department, including ...

- **Margaret**, an elderly lady suffering from severe lower abdominal pains. Initial assessment indicated a possibility of **bowel cancer**.

- **Jasmin**, a three year old suffering from a severe headache, a high temperature and stiffness of the neck. Initial assessment indicated a strong possibility of **meningitis**.

- **Paul**, a 52 year old who had been involved in a fall whilst climbing a ladder at work. Initial assessment suggested **broken bones in his right arm and shoulder**.

- **Abdul**, a 16 year old who was suffering from severe pain in the lower side of his back, on both sides. He had a fever and was shivering, with some vomiting. Initial assessment suggested a possible **kidney infection**.

- **Ray**, a 65 year old complaining of a crushing pain in the centre of his chest, with breathlessness and some dizziness. Initial assessment suggested a **heart attack**.

- **Abla**, nearly a year old, was brought in by her parents because she was breathless and seemed to be in constant pain. Her fingers and toes were swollen and the intial assessment indicated **sickle cell anaemia**.

- **Bandhura**, an 18 year old, had recently returned from a backpacking tour in India. She said she had been suffering from fever, chills and headache. Initial assessment suggested possible **malaria**.

- **Albert**, in his eighties, had a very flushed face and had complained of general aches and pains, dizziness and a lack of energy. Initial assessment suggested '**flu**.

- **Vicky**, recently retired, had diarrhoea and abdominal cramps. She had just been in hospital on a course of antibiotics. Initial assessment suggested possible *C. diff* infection (*Clostridium difficile*).

- **Luke**, a 56 year old who was quite overweight, complained of blurred vision. He said that these days he always seemed thirsty and had to go to the toilet a lot. Initial assessment suggested **type 2 diabetes**.

Task 1

Select some of the cases in the scenario above and identify and describe two biological and two physical procedures that could be used in diagnosis.

If you complete task 1 correctly you will meet grading criterion P1

Task 2

Explain the scientific principles underlying each of the procedures.

If you complete task 2 correctly you will meet grading criterion M1

Task 3

Evaluate the advantages and disadvantages of using the identified procedures for the chosen cases.

If you complete task 3 correctly you will meet grading criterion D1

Task 4

Identify the therapeutic drugs relevant to treating three named illnesses. Use the examples above or other illnesses of your own choice.

If you complete task 4 correctly you will meet grading criterion P2

Task 5

Describe how the therapeutic drugs are used to treat the named illnesses.

If you complete task 5 correctly you will meet grading criterion M2

Task 6

Explain why the actions of the therapeutic drugs are used to treat the named illnesses.

If you complete task 6 correctly you will meet grading criterion D2

Task 7

Using some of the examples suggested in the scenario, describe two therapeutic techniques that could be used in treatment.

If you complete task 7 correctly you will meet grading criterion P3

Task 8

Explain the functions of each of the techniques in the treatment of the illness/condition.

If you complete task 8 correctly you will meet grading criterion M3

Task 9

Evaluate the reasons why some individuals, religions and cultures may choose not to take advantage of all types of available treatments.

If you complete task 9 correctly you will meet grading criterion D3

Guidelines

Your teacher will give you further guidelines. For example, they may wish you to write a short report or article, give a presentation or produce a poster.

Make sure you clearly indicate which cases you choose for each of the biological and physical procedures used for diagnosis. If you wish to attempt Task 3 for distinction level (D1), you should choose the procedures carefully, so that you can have good examples of advantages and disadvantages to discuss.

P1   **Identify** each procedure by naming it and linking it to one of the cases.

   Describe each procedure by stating:

   •   what it is for

   •   how it is carried out

   •   what results are possible

   •   what the possible results would indicate.

M1   You will need to explain how and why each procedure works.

D1   You will need to weigh up the possible advantages and disadvantages of the procedures, taking into account the individuals concerned.

If you wish to achieve the merit and/or distinction levels (Tasks 5 and 6 for M2 and D2), choose the drugs carefully so you can find the information you need to describe their formulation and explain how they work.

P2   **Identify** the drugs by naming the diseases and the drugs used to treat them.

M2   **Describe** how the drugs are used by describing the formulation of each drug and the route by which it is administered.

D2   **Explain** by giving details of how the drugs work to alleviate symptoms or cure the cause of each illness.

Task 9 (D3) can be considered separately from the scenario and Tasks 7 and 8 (P3 and M3), though you may get ideas from the case studies. You will need to research and use examples of techniques which some people object to because of their individual beliefs, upbringing or religion.

P3   **Describe** means that you need to state what each procedure involves and how it is carried out to treat an illness or condition. Choose and name two illnesses or conditions from the scenario and describe one technique for each.

M3   **Explain the functions** means that you need to give details of what your two chosen techniques do and how they work to treat the symptoms or cure the illness or condition.

D3   **Evaluate** means that you need to assess the judgements that have to be made. How do beliefs and values affect which treatments people will accept and which they will reject? Use examples to show how individual, cultural and religious beliefs affect choice of acceptable treatments.

NEW DRUGS

1: Why do we need new drugs?

Do some research to find reasons why new drugs are needed in one particular area.

Choose from the following examples:

- **Cancer**
- **Heart disease**
- **Malaria**
- **MRSA**
- *C. diff* (*Clostridium difficile*)

Compare your notes with anyone else who has researched the same example.

Record your findings below.

Example:

_____

Reasons why new drugs are needed:

_____

_____

_____

_____

_____

_____

_____

_____

2: Selection of compounds and pre-clinical trials

Using robots, millions of new chemical compounds can be made in a short space of time. Scientists look at diseases and potential methods for treating them. Computer modelling is used to see if a compound has the properties that will be effective. Promising compounds can then be tested further.

Explain what is meant by **in vitro** and **in vivo** testing.

_____

_____

_____

_____

How can in vitro testing be used to test the effectiveness of a potential new drug?

You can carry out your own investigation to test the effect of chemicals on the growth of bacteria.

Investigating chemicals that protect against micro-organisms

Health and safety

A risk assessment must be carried out for all procedures before you start work. Biological material should be handled with caution. Wear a laboratory coat and report any spills. Follow your teacher's instructions for disposal of materials.

You will need

4 x Petri dishes containing agar seeded with bacteria [BIOHAZARD] • permanent marker • different antiseptic and disinfectant solutions or pre-impregnated antibiotic discs • distilled water • pair of metal forceps • filter paper discs (made with stationery hole punch) • Bunsen burner • biohazard tape

Method

1   Collect the equipment you need. Set up a Bunsen burner on a heatproof mat.

     When you are working in aseptic conditions the air hole of the Bunsen burner should be open and the flame blue. Work close to the flame. When you are not using the Bunsen burner, the air hole should be closed and the flame yellow.

2   Label the bottom of the four Petri dishes that have been spread with bacteria [BIOHAZARD].

     Label one plate **water** and the other three plates with the names of the antiseptic, disinfectant or antibiotic discs used.

3   Use the metal forceps to pick up a filter paper disc. Dip it into the bottle of distilled water. Drain the filter paper on the side of the bottle until it stops dripping.

4   Quickly but carefully lift the lid of the Petri dish just enough to allow you access and put the filter paper disc in the centre of the dish. Use the metal forceps to press the disc down gently. Take care not to damage the agar.

5   Briefly pass the metal forceps through the Bunsen burner flame to kill any bacteria that might have been picked up from the surface of the agar plate. Allow them to cool.

6   Repeat steps 3 and 4 for the three antiseptics or disinfectants you're investigating. Think about how you will make sure that you don't contaminate any of the plates with the previous sample used. Antibiotic discs will already contain antibiotic and can be placed directly on the plates (no soaking necessary).

7   Fasten the Petri dish lid with four short strips of biohazard tape. Incubate your plates at 25 °C for two days.

In the next lesson ...

Look at the agar plates you prepared. DO NOT OPEN THEM.

Draw what you see on your agar plates on the diagrams below.

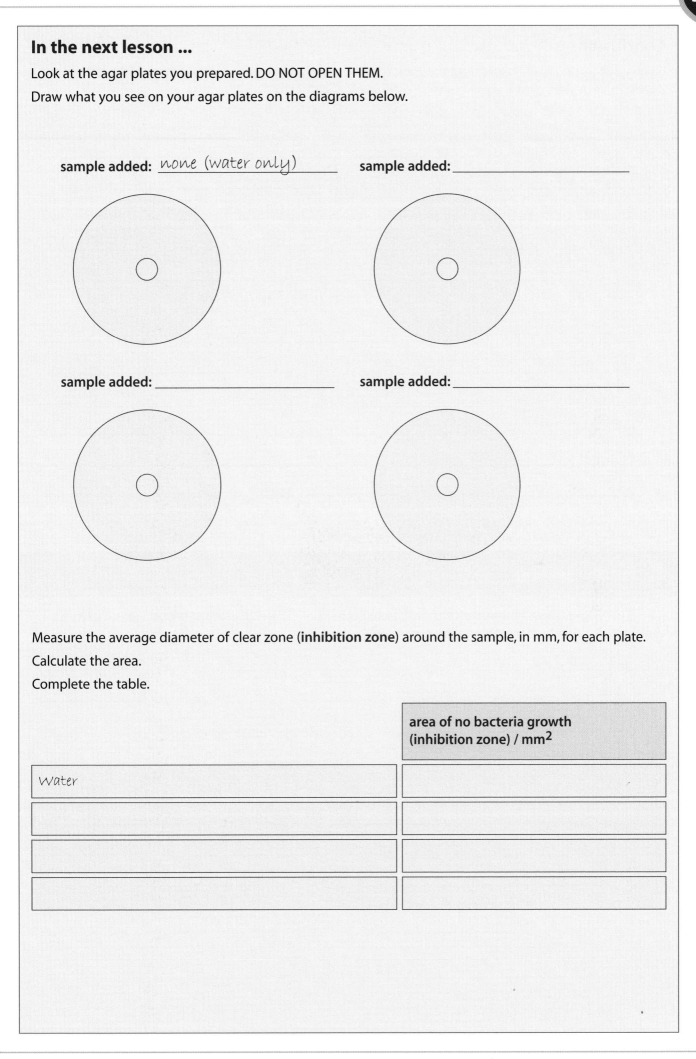

sample added: _none (water only)_

sample added: _____

sample added: _____

sample added: _____

Measure the average diameter of clear zone (**inhibition zone**) around the sample, in mm, for each plate.

Calculate the area.

Complete the table.

	area of no bacteria growth (inhibition zone) / mm^2
Water	

Conclusions

If you were testing new chemical compounds, which ones (if any) would you send forward for further testing? Use evidence from your results to justify your decisions.

_____

_____

_____

_____

_____

_____

_____

_____

_____

_____

_____

_____

_____

_____

3: Further testing

If in vitro testing shows anti-microbial activity, what other pre-clinical trials must be carried out before clinical trials using humans? Why is this necessary?

_____

_____

_____

_____

_____

_____

_____

_____

_____

_____

_____

_____

ASSIGNMENT – DEVELOPING THERAPEUTIC DRUGS

Scenario

You are a technician working for a major pharmaceutical company. Your local paper has a weekly column, *Science for all*. Your boss has asked you to write three short articles for the column on the development of new drugs. They have chosen you for your ability to communicate clearly in straightforward language that the person in the street can understand. The articles are to be:

- *How we get new drugs*
- *Why new drugs are hard to find*
- *New drugs and the law*

Task 1

Describe how a new drug is developed, from the moment it's identified to its production and marketing.

If you complete task 1 correctly you will meet grading criterion P4

Task 2

Explain the reasons why very few potential drugs make it all the way through the development process to become licensed drugs.

If you complete task 2 correctly you will meet grading criterion M4

Task 3

Give an overview of the legal requirements affecting the development of a new drug in the UK.

If you complete task 3 correctly you will meet grading criterion D4

Guidelines

Your teacher will give you further guidelines including the deadlines for this assignment.

P4 **Describe** requires you to indicate what happens at each stage in the process.

M4 **Explain** means that you should give reasons:

- why a potential drug can fail to progress at each stage of development
- why so few make it through to the end.

D4 **Review** means you should describe the legal requirements and comment on their purpose.

You should:

- write your articles in a concise format which can be understood by an intelligent non-expert
- use terminology correctly, but explain it where necessary.

FACTORS AFFECTING TREATMENTS

1: Not all existing treatments are available to all people

What are the main reasons why some people can receive a particular treatment but others, suffering from the same condition, cannot?

List at least four factors which affect the availability of drugs and treatments to individuals and groups.

_____

_____

_____

_____

_____

_____

_____

_____

2: Case study

Research one example of a drug or treatment that isn't available to all.

Write a short report to summarise and explain the factors which affect its availability.

Hint: choose a good example so you can easily find the information you need.

_____

_____

_____

_____

_____

_____

_____

_____

_____

_____

_____

_____

ASSIGNMENT – DRUG AND TREATMENT AVAILABILITY

Introduction

- Most of the work you need to do on this unit can be concentrated on your final assignment for assessment of P5, M5 and D5.

- At this stage, you should plan your work carefully to try to get the best overall grade for this unit.

- Decide which level you want to aim for, bearing in mind how successful you have been with your other assessments. Discuss this with your teacher.

Scenario

You are working part-time in a pharmacy. The pharmacist is concerned that clients:

- often ask why they can't have a certain drug or type of treatment that they have heard of

- fail to check on the safe use of their medication by reading the information leaflets they are given

- complain when their doctor won't give them a prescription for a drug, when they know someone else who is getting it.

She asks you to make a large poster for clients to read while they are waiting for their prescriptions.

Task 1

Under the heading *Availability of drugs and treatments*, list and briefly describe the factors that can affect whether a drug or treatment is available to a patient.

If you complete task 1 correctly you will meet grading criterion P5

Task 2

Under the heading *Drugs and you - please read the guidelines provided*, explain in general terms how all drug treatments involve an element of risk.

If you complete task 2 correctly you will meet grading criterion M5

Task 3

Under the heading *Drug availability - a matter of judgement*, use examples to explain why:

- drugs are made available for some people but not to others

- this will always be a controversial issue.

If you complete task 3 correctly you will meet grading criterion D5

Guidelines

P5 Think about the reasons why some drugs are freely available, some are restricted to certain people and others are not legally available at all.

M5 You may find it helpful to list the ways in which drugs:

- may not have the expected or desired effects

- how they may have unexpected and/or undesirable effects.

Use examples to explain the risks that you identify.

D5 What makes the decisions so controversial? Look for examples in the news; try to explain the controversy when someone receives drugs but another person does not.

ESSENTIAL KNOWLEDGE AND DATA

Symptoms

If you're ill, you may go to the doctor. The doctor will **diagnose** the cause of your illness by looking for and carrying out basic tests for **symptoms**.

Symptoms ...

- are changes in normal body appearance or function - what is *wrong* with you
- indicate the cause of the illness.

The doctor may send you for further tests that require specialists.

By diagnosing the cause of the illness, the doctor can select the correct treatment.

The doctor's diagnosis may involve **biological** or **physical** factors.

Biological diagnosis includes ...

- identification of organisms causing disease
- inspection of blood or other tissues for cell abnormalities
- chemical analysis of blood, sputum (*phlegm*), urine or faeces
- genetic investigations.

Physical diagnosis includes ...

- body temperature measurements
- blood pressure measurements
- X-rays
- CT (computerised tomography) scans
- MRI (magnetic resonance imaging) scans
- endoscopy.

Biological diagnosis

Pathology is the study of disease. A pathologist is expert in recognising and understanding the changes that take place in the human body during disease.

Pathology technicians routinely carry out laboratory tests on samples taken from patients, to reveal the causes of an illness.

The results of the tests help doctors to decide on treatment or cause of death. This is based on the changes in tissues or body fluids from their normal appearance or chemistry.

The Department of Health estimates that about 70% of NHS diagnoses depend on pathology tests.

Testing for organisms

Viruses, bacteria and parasites such as protists, fungi and various animals can cause disease.

These harmful organisms are called **pathogens**. They damage tissues and release toxins (poisons).

Such organisms should not be present in the body.

If you can find them, you have a very direct method of diagnosing an illness.

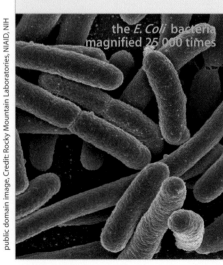

the *E. Coli* bacteria magnified 25 000 times

public domain image, Credit: Rocky Mountain Laboratories, NIAID, NIH

Viruses ...

cause many human diseases, from the common cold and influenza to chicken pox, mumps, rubella, polio, rabies and AIDS. They are hard to find:

- about 20 nm to 400 nm in size
- can only be seen using an electron microscope
- spend most of the time hidden inside host cells.

an electron micrograph of influenza virus particles

public domain image, credit: CDC/Dr F A Murphy

A nasal swab can be taken from a suspected 'flu victim and the viruses cultured so they can be identified. Viruses need living cells to reproduce, so they are added to a thin layer of host cells in a culture dish. Each cell infected by a virus is killed, forming holes in the cell layer known as **plaques**. Counting the number of plaques gives an estimate of the number of viruses in the original sample.

Other viruses, in suitable samples, can be cultured the same way, but this is an expensive and time consuming process.

Viruses can be isolated and prepared so they can be viewed using an electron microscope. This is only done if it is a nasty disease that is hard to diagnose, like Ebola haemorrhagic fever (pronounced hem-or-rajik).

Virus culture needs large laboratories, expensive equipment and trained specialists including technicians, molecular biologists and **virologists**.

The normal way to detect viruses is much simpler and cheaper - by testing for antibodies that a person makes in response to a virus infection. This is explained in the section on *Chemical tests*.

Bacteria ...

are very diverse and also cause a wide range of disease: many kinds of food poisoning, whooping cough, diphtheria, tetanus, meningitis, tuberculosis, anthrax and syphilis.

Although only about 0.5 μm to 4 μm long and invisible to the naked eye, they can be seen using an optical microscope or grown on culture plates to form visible colonies.

Shape gives a first clue to their identity. They may be:

- spherical cocci (one is a coccus)
- rod shaped bacilli (bacillus)
- spiral spirilla (spirillum)
- comma shaped vibriae (vibrio).

Bacteria are stained with dyes such as methylene blue to make them easily visible using a microscope. A technique called **Gram staining** leaves some bacteria purple and others red. This distinguishes them as Gram positive or Gram negative respectively.

Given the nutrients and temperature they need, bacteria can divide every 20 minutes. There will be visible colonies of billions of cells within a day or two. When grown in plates on solid, jelly-like agar, the colour, shape and texture (e.g. glossy or powdery) of colonies is used to identify the species of bacteria present.

Selective media, which provide special conditions (e.g. pH or nutrients) can also be used. For example, *Salmonella* bacteria are Gram negative bacilli which grow well to form white colonies in agar with added bile salts.

Many other bacteria are inhibited by the bile salts.

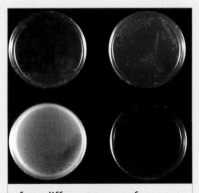

four different types of nutrient agar that have been inoculated with bacteria 24 hours earlier

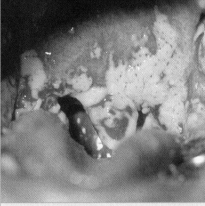

oral thrush - a fungal infection

public domain image, credit: CDC

Parasites ...

may be protists, fungi or animals.

- Protists causing disease include malarial and sleeping sickness parasites. The adult organisms can be seen in human blood.
- Fungi, including ringworm, athlete's foot and thrush often form visible infections. Fungi that hide inside the body are more difficult to diagnose.
- Animals include flatworms, tapeworms and roundworms. Microscopic roundworms (filarial worms) can be found in blood. They can block lymph nodes and cause the swellings of elephantiasis. Gut parasites are most commonly diagnosed by looking for eggs or adults in faeces.

Looking for cell abnormalities

Pathogens are not the only cause of disease. Other factors can harm tissues and their normal functioning.

Cancers, toxins (poisons), inherited defects and nutritional problems (excess as well as deficiencies) cause changes in the appearance of cells and tissues.

The process of taking a sample of body cells for analysis is called a **biopsy**.

Punch biopsy ...

utilises a special tool that removes cells from the surface of the skin (e.g. from a mole). It is also used on other organs revealed during surgery. (Alternatively, a small piece of tissue is cut out with a scalpel.)

Scraping ...

is the simplest biopsy method. For example, a smear test sample is taken with a special spatula to remove epithelial (lining) cells from the cervix (neck of the womb). The *Pap* technique is used to stain a smear of the cells on a microscope slide. Abnormal, precancerous cells stain differently to normal cells and typically have enlarged nuclei.

Note: this is not diagnosis of disease at this stage. Screening for cervical cancer is available in the UK every three to five years to **all** women between the ages of 25 and 64 to prevent cancer **before** it develops. Cancer of the cervix is the second most common cancer among women worldwide. Screening takes it down to eleventh in the UK, saving 4500 women's lives every year.

Endoscopic biopsy ...

utlises a thin, flexible tube with a lighted camera to see inside the body.

Surgery is avoided if tissues can be reached through one of the body's existing entries, such as the throat or anus.

Tiny cutting tools are used to remove a sample of tissue.

Needle biopsy ...

is used to sample blood and other tissue from organs beneath the skin, such as breast lumps, kidneys or bone marrow.

Haemotology is the study of diseases of the blood. A blood smear can be prepared for microscopic examination by spreading it over the surface of a slide. It's usually stained to make cells and their structures more visible. Inspection includes looking for incorrect **numbers** of blood cells. Any change in *normal* blood cells or the presence of foreign organisms is likely to be linked to a disease.

cell abnormalities found in the blood (changes to blood cells)	some associated diseases
large numbers of white cells	may be response to infection or due to leukaemia (a type of cancer)
fewer than normal red blood cells, or red cells vary in size	anaemia
low in platelets	leukaemia
sickle-shaped red blood cells	sickle cell anaemia
parasites inside red blood cells	malaria

Chemical analysis

It's easy, quick and safe to obtain samples of **blood, sputum (*spit*), urine** and **faeces**. In ill health, these often contain disease-causing organisms or chemicals that the pathology technician can test for. Chemical tests include ...

Blood cholesterol levels

High cholesterol levels in the blood can increase the risk of cardiovascular disease. This leads to heart attacks or strokes (burst or blocked blood vessels in the brain).

You may be tested if:

- other factors, such as diabetes, family history, smoking or high blood pressure increase your risk of a heart attack
- you have a heart attack (note: this *reduces* blood cholesterol, so the test is at least six weeks afterwards).

If your **total** cholesterol is more than 5 mmol/dm^3 of blood, treatment such as dietary changes or drugs to lower your cholesterol may be recommended.

It's also possible to test for:

- HDL-cholesterol (which is *good* cholesterol that goes to the liver for excretion) and
- LDL-cholesterol (which is *bad* cholesterol, linked to disease).

Acid fast test for sputum (and other samples)

This is a test for the mycobacteria that cause tuberculosis (TB). Sputum is the mucus that is brought up from the lungs. Coughing is suppressed during sleep, so it is best collected first thing in the morning when the lungs are being cleared of fluid. TB can infect other regions of the body, so this test can also be used on blood, urine, faeces, bone marrow, or tissue biopsies.

This test is a differential staining technique like Gram staining. A small amount of the sample is placed on a microscope slide and heated with a stain (dye). The slide is then washed with an acid solution, and a second stain is applied. Mycobacteria are acid fast and have a coat that retains the first stain. Other bacteria lose the first stain (non-acid fast), but show up the colour of the second stain.

C. difficile toxins in faeces

Medical technicians call faeces tests *stool tests*.

This test is often done when vulnerable people have diarrhoea following a course of antibiotics. A course of antibiotics usually kills the *friendly* bacteria that suppress harmful bacteria in your gut. A strain of *Clostridium difficile* is resistant to most antibiotics. So it multiplies, releasing toxins (poisons) that damage the wall of the large intestine, causing diarrhoea. *C. difficile* has become a major killer in hospitals around the world. It infects weakened old and sick people.

As many organisms can cause diarrhoea, the test has to be very specific. Antibodies are highly specific and can be used in this and many other tests for individual chemicals, including in pregnancy and HIV testing. A system called an **ELISA** is used (short for **E**nzyme-**L**inked **I**mmuno**S**orbent **A**ssay). The *immune* reaction is linked to enzyme activity, so that a visible positive result can be seen. This test detects the presence of toxins produced by *C.difficile* in faeces.

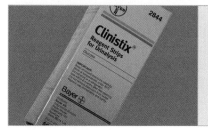

Glucose in urine

Glucose should not be present in urine. If it is, it may be caused by high blood glucose levels due to a lack of insulin in diabetes.

A test strip with an enzyme that makes glucose react (such as *Clinistix*) is dipped into the urine. A change from colourless to purple indicates glucose is present.

Genetic investigations

In the UK, cystic fibrosis (CF) is the most common, life-threatening inherited condition in Caucasians (*white* people). It is still quite rare, affecting about 500 people in the UK and one birth in about every 2500.

You need to know the principles of genetics to understand how conditions like CF are inherited.

- CF is caused by a single recessive allele (the form a gene takes).
- Huntington's chorea is caused by a single dominant allele.
- Red-green colour blindness is caused by a sex-linked allele found only on X-chromosomes.

Family history counselling

A genetic counsellor advises couples about the risks to their children and the action that they can take, if they have a relative who suffers from an inherited condition. DNA testing is expensive, so family history counselling is usually done first to see if testing is desirable. The risk to the child depends on how the condition is inherited and which relatives are affected. For example, for a child to inherit CF, it must get a recessive allele from **both** parents.

Recessive conditions like this can be inherited from parents who are not themselves affected, but are **carriers**.

Inheritance of CF

The diagram shows that, if both parents are carriers, there is a one in four chance they'll have a child with CF (or other recessive condition).

This chance averages out, so some families may be lucky, while others are unlucky. For example, a family with three children may have two with CF. Other carrier parents will have no children with CF.

	mother Ff (carrier)	
	mother's eggs	
	F	f
F	FF	Ff
f	fF carrier	ff cystic fibrosis

(father Ff (carrier), father's sperm)

allele symbol	effect (Phenotype)
F	normal mucus production
f	thick mucus clogs lungs and digestive tract

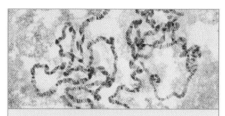

DNA analysis

DNA probes test for the presence of the mutant DNA base sequences that cause CF.

DNA for testing can be obtained from cheek cells in a mouthwash sample or from white bloodcells in a blood sample.

If both parents are carriers, they may opt for IVF (in vitro fertilisation, literally *in glass* outside the body). This gives embryos which are tested at the three day stage. Healthy embryos are then inserted into the mother's uterus.

Diagnosis of CF

All newborn children in the UK can be tested for CF.

In the **sweat test**:

- sweating is stimulated by a small electric current through the skin of the forearm
- sweat is collected on filter paper
- the sweat is tested for above--normal levels of chloride
- a positive test **shows** chloride >60 mmol/dm^3.

Parents may opt for normal pregnancy and have the fetus tested in the womb by **amniocentesis** or **CVS** (chorionic villus sampling).

Fetal cells in the amniotic fluid that surrounds the fetus, or from the finger-like projections from the placenta, provide DNA for testing.

These cells are also used to check for conditions, such as Down's Syndrome (in which an extra chromosome is present).

These tests are only carried out if the parents are willing to consider an abortion - they believe that the child's quality of life is likely to be severely affected.

Vital signs

Measurements of the body's basic functions or **vital signs** are useful for detecting or monitoring medical problems. Medical professionals usually monitor:

- body temperature
- pulse rate
- respiration rate (rate of breathing)
- blood pressure.

These measurements are quick and easy to take in a hospital or doctor's surgery, at home, at the site of a medical emergency or elsewhere. They give useful information about your general health and give clues to help diagnose illnesses. Changes in vital signs indicate whether you are getting better or if your illness is getting worse.

Medical imaging

Medical imaging is the process of examining parts of the patient's body which are not normally visible. These methods of physical diagnosis include:

- X-rays
- CT (computerised tomography) scans
- MRI (magnetic resonance imaging) scans
- endoscopy.

They all require specialised equipment and skilled operators. For example, you might train to be a Radiographer or Medical Physicist.

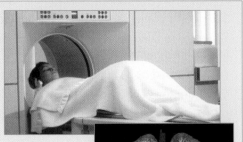

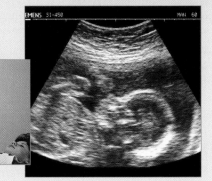

Norms

In a healthy person, body temperature and blood pressure vary, but within controlled limits.

Homeostasis is automatic. It is the feedback mechanism keeping conditions inside the body within healthy limits or **norms**. Norms are the boundaries within which the body systems work efficiently. Body temperature and blood pressure must be controlled.

Body temperature

Temperature is measured with a thermometer or a thermal probe with digital readout. Less accurate measurements can also be obtained using thermochromic thermometers, which change colour.

A healthy, *normal* body temperature was considered to be 37.0 °C. Now we know that many factors cause it to vary, including:

gender • age • time of day • recent activity, e.g. exercise • wearing heavy clothing • the stage of the menstrual cycle • pregnancy

Temperature also depends on where the reading is taken.

- In the UK the usual mouth (oral) measurement gave a norm of 37.0 °C.
- In Russia 36.6 °C was the norm, based on armpit (axillary) temperature.

Both these measurements used slow-responding glass thermometers. Nowadays, rapid-acting infrared ear probes measure ear drum (tympanic) temperature. This is about 0.5 °C higher than mouth temperature and close to the body core temperature - the temperature of the internal organs.

According to NHS Direct:

'A normal temperature is between 36-36.8 °C (96.8-98.24 °F). In children, any temperature of 38 °C (100.4 °F) or above is considered high and is classed as a fever.'

Fevers

Fevers are usually caused by infections or other illness. A rise in body temperature stimulates natural defences and slows down the reproduction of viruses.

Common causes of fever are:

'flu • ear infections • tonsillitis • kidney infections • childhood diseases (such as measles, mumps, chicken pox, whooping cough)

Young children and old people can't regulate their body temperature very well, so too many clothes, in a hot environment, can sometimes cause a fever. Some fevers are caused by medicines including antibiotics or by severe trauma, such as in a heart attack or stroke.

Blood pressure

Blood pressure is measured in millimetres of mercury (mmHg) using a **sphygmomanometer**. This has an inflatable cuff that wraps round the upper arm.

Old blood pressure meters used a column of mercury to measure pressure in the cuff. The health professional used a stethoscope to listen for blood flow stopping and starting as the arteries were squeezed and released. Now, they use digital machines. These automatically inflate and deflate the cuff and record the pressure.

When your blood pressure is measured, two readings are taken:

Systolic pressure is the higher measurement, when the heart contracts and pumps blood out. It's the reading when inflating the cuff stops the flow.

Diastolic pressure is the lower measurement, when the heart is relaxed and filling up with blood. It's the reading when the flow starts again on releasing the cuff.

The readings are given as two numbers with the systolic pressure first, e.g. 120/80 mmHg (stated as: *one hundred and twenty over eighty*.)

High blood pressure

Having high blood pressure increases the risk of heart attack or stroke. High blood pressure (**hypertension**) is defined as a systolic pressure of 140 mmHg or more and/or a diastolic pressure of 90 mmHg or more. Lower blood pressure puts less strain on the heart and artery walls, so a *healthy* adult blood pressure is considered to be 120/80 or less. High blood pressure is common, but low blood pressure is rare.

Blood pressure varies so it's measured when the patient is at rest. High blood pressure is only diagnosed if it **persists** (usually three measurements over three months).

Anyone with high blood pressure should consider lifestyle changes such as improved diet and more exercise. Drugs are recommended if there's a sustained systolic pressure of 160 mmHg or more and/or diastolic pressure of 100 mmHg or more (sometimes called *stage 2 high blood pressure*).

Risk factors associated with high blood pressure include:

- **getting older** • **being male** • **having relatives with high blood pressure**
- **being overweight** • **drinking excessive alcohol** • **stress** • **smoking**
- **lack of exercise** • **being of Afro-Caribbean origin**
- **being British with South Asian origin**

Symptoms

Most people with high blood pressure have no symptoms. In rare cases, blood pressure can rise without warning to reach 220/120 mmHg. Urgent treatment is necessary. Symptoms of severe high blood pressure include:

- **confusion**
- **severe headache**
- **nausea**
- **difficulty seeing**
- **feeling very sleepy.**

Heat stroke and hypothermia

In a fever, the person feels cold at high body temperatures because the infection sets the body thermostat higher. Although this is uncomfortable, it helps the body fight infection.

In heat stroke, the body temperature is higher than set by its thermostat. It continues to rise, as the body loses control. Dehydration occurs and the skin is dry, even under the armpits. The person feels very hot. This is a life--threatening medical emergency.

In hypothermia, body temperature can fall dangerously low. Babies and small children have a higher surface area to mass ratio, which means that they can lose heat more easily than adults. Older adults regulate body temperature less effectively. They are also at greater risk of developing hypothermia in the cold.

The key body temperatures are shown in the table.

temperature / °C	symptoms
44	almost certain death (some people have survived up to 46.5 °C)
43	death or serious brain damage, convulsions, heart attack
42	coma likely
40-41	profuse sweating, weakness, fainting, dehydration, vomiting and headache, confusion
39	high fever: severe sweating, very red, fast heart and breathing rates, possible exhaustion
38	fever: sweating, uncomfortable
37	normal
36	possible shivering, but may be normal
35	intense shivering, pale skin
34	blueness and confusion, severe shivering, loss of finger movement
33	severe confusion, shivering may stop, sleepiness
32	sleepiness becoming coma, complete confusion and delerium
31	coma, slow heart and breathing rates
28	may appear dead, breathing may stop
24-26	death usual due to heart or respiratory arrest (some survivors down to 14.2 °C)

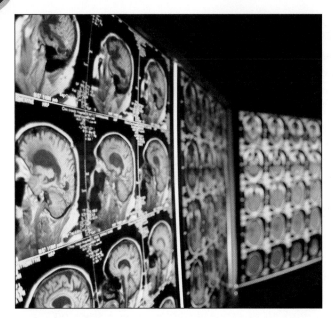

Body imaging methods

Monitoring body temperature and blood pressure tells you about the functioning of the body in quite general terms. Some things that go wrong are visible from the surface, for example skin cancers. Sometimes you need to take a closer look under the surface. Non-invasive or minimally invasive imaging techniques can be used to look inside the body. Without these, invasive surgery would be necessary, opening up the body to look inside, with more risk and trauma for the patient.

Each technique requires a trained expert to use it effectively. Techniques include:

- X-rays
- CT (computerised tomography) scans
- MRI (magnetic resonance imaging) scans
- endoscopy.

X-rays

If you've ever had a broken bone or tooth decay, then you've probably had an *X-ray*. X-rays are:

- short wavelength electromagnetic waves
- generated in an X-ray tube by firing electrons at a tungsten target
- able to pass easily through soft tissue like skin and muscle, giving darker images
- absorbed by dense tissues like tooth and bone, giving lighter images.

Radiographers use X-rays to obtain:

- still photographic or digital images
- moving images
- images which are 2-D only.

Bone fractures and tooth decay can be seen clearly, quickly and easily.

Other problems with bones and joints can be diagnosed, for example dislocations, arthritis or osteoporosis (thinning of the bone tissue).

Tumours and areas of fluid build-up or scar tissue can be detected, for example in the lungs in pneumonia or tuberculosis (TB). X-rays to look for breast tumours are called *mammograms*. Those used to detect abnormalities in blood vessels, such as narrowing of the coronary artery, are *angiograms*.

Blood vessels and the gut are normally difficult to see, but can be shown up by using materials that absorb X-rays. For example, you could give a patient a barium meal to show gut problems or inject a dye to show narrowing of coronary arteries (an *angiogram*).

Swallowed objects can also be detected.

Although X-rays are widely available, quick and relatively cheap to use, they are high energy and may cause tissue damage or mutations in DNA. This can lead to infertility or cancer if used too frequently.

Modern X-ray machines use very safe, very low dosages, but many early investigators died from cancer.

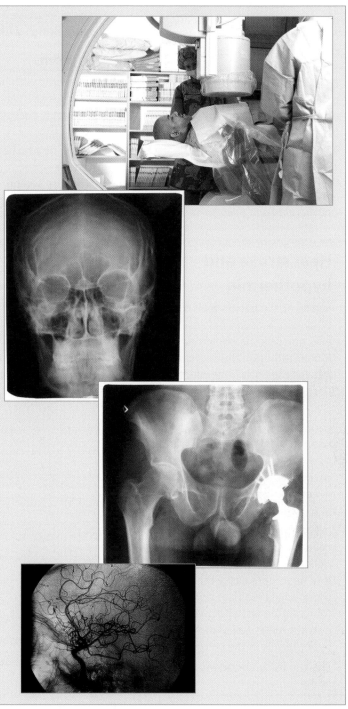

CT scans

CT or CAT (computerised axial tomography) scans use X-rays, but a very much more expensive machine is used.

The patient passes through a ring--shaped tunnel in which X-ray tubes and detectors rotate. Images are built up in layers or slices.

A computer assembles 3D images which can be viewed from any angle. The computer software also enhances contrast between tissues, so that soft tissues such as brain or lung tissue can be seen.

CT scanning gives much more detailed images of structures inside the body. But it exposes patients to higher levels of X-rays than conventional X-ray machines. It also requires very expensive machinery and facilities, and so is much less readily available.

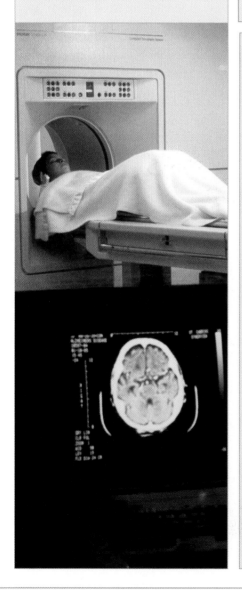

MRI scans

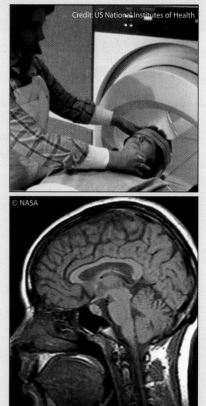

Credit: US National Institutes of Health

© NASA

Magnetic resonance imaging uses a very powerful magnetic field and radio waves. These make the hydrogen atoms in the body resonate at a particular frequency which the scanner detects. The scanner is a circular superconducting magnet.

Detectors record the position and abundance of the hydrogen atoms. These vary according to the amount of water present in different body tissues. A computer converts this data into 3-D images of the internal organs.

The strong magnetic fields and weak radio waves are thought to be completely harmless. They give clear images of the soft tissues of internal organs, showing up injuries and cancer tumours.

Like CT scanning, MRI requires very expensive equipment and facilities, and so is less readily available. Also, the patient passes through a very narrow, noisy tunnel, which some people find disturbing.

Endoscopy

A flexible endoscope uses optical fibres to obtain an image from inside the body.

A narrow tube is passed in through one of the bodies natural openings, such as the throat or anus, or through a surgical *keyhole*.

A bundle of ultra-thin optical fibres make a flexible tube which can be manipulated into areas of the body, such as the stomach or lungs. A light source illuminates the area under investigation. The image is seen through an eyepiece or transmitted to a TV screen, using a camera at the end of the optical fibres.

Rigid endoscopes are sometimes used, e.g. for looking inside joints, when a short distance is involved.

Optical fibres rely on the fact that light is usually refracted as it passes from one medium into another, but at a certain critical angle it is totally internally reflected and can't escape. So, a beam of light will pass all the way along an optical fibre, even when it's bent.

optical fibre

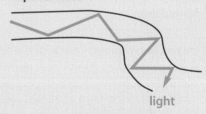

light

The fibres have to be in the same position at each end of the cable, so a picture can build up out of the dots of light. The more fibres you have in your bundle, the more dots of light and the sharper the image.

Although it can cause some discomfort, endoscopy is simple, cheap and easy to perform. Clear images of problems such as ulcers in the gut or tumours in the lungs can be seen.

Simple instruments can be added at the end of the endoscope, for example to stop bleeding or remove tissue samples (biopsy). Very rarely, an endoscope can cause damage to the areas it is passing through.

Therapeutic drugs

Drugs may be used as medicines to treat a wide range of disorders. Sometimes they help the healing process. Other times they alleviate symptoms.

Penicillin, for example, is an **antibiotic** which kills bacteria. Aspirin, on the other hand, is an **analgesic** (pain killer) and **antipyretic** (reduces body temperature during a fever).

Relieving symptoms is not always a good thing. Fever is the body's response to a virus infection. A higher than normal body temperature helps to slow down virus reproduction. So, some doctors think that giving children antipyretics will make, for example, their 'flu last longer.

Drugs include:

- **analgesics e.g. paracetamol, aspirin, ibuprofen, codeine**
- **anti-inflammatories e.g. ibuprofen**
- **antibiotics e.g. penicillin**
- **anti-histamines e.g. acrivastine**
- **chemical replacements e.g. insulin**
- **cytological (cytotoxic or chemotherapy)**
- **antidepressants**
- **stimulants**
- **sedatives**
- **heart drugs.**

Correct diagnosis means that, if appropriate, a suitable type of drug can be chosen by the doctor and dispensed by the pharmacist.

The **formulation** of a drug is the way it's made up for use. This is designed to suit:

- what it's being used to treat
- the way it works
- how it gets to its site of action.

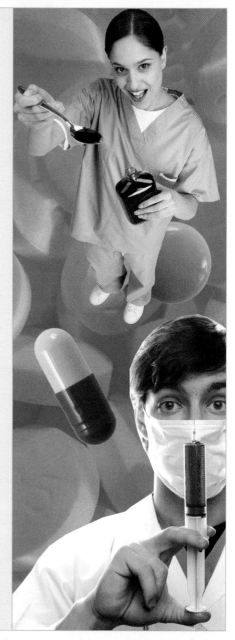

formulation	route
creams or ointments - thickened substances containing drugs, can be spread over the surface of the skin	topical
tablet - pill in the form of a small solid pellet enclosing a known amount of drug	oral
capsule - pill in the form of a small soluble container enclosing a known amount of drug	oral
oral liquid - a solution or suspension that can be taken by mouth and can be given in a measured dose	oral
injected liquid - a solution or suspension that can be given in a measured dose (injection may be carried out using a syringe, a pump or a drip)	intravenous injection - into the blood in a vein subcutaneous injection - under the skin into the tissues

Uses of drugs

Here is a summary of the uses of a variety of drug types - and the way they work ...

ANALGESICS

examples	uses	action	formulation/route
Opiods or narcotics e.g. codeine, morphine. Non-opioids or non-narcotics e.g. paracetamol, aspirin, ibuprofen	To ease moderate to severe pain e.g. following operations, serious injuries or painful terminal illnesses. To ease mild to moderate pain such as headache, backache, toothache, muscle and joint pains, period pains.	Block the transmission of pain signals in the spinal cord and brain. Codeine is less powerful than morphine. Act on pain at the site of the injury by preventing prostaglandin production in damaged tissues. Prostaglandins cause inflammation and swelling leading to pain, acting on nerve endings, they send pain signals to the brain. Paracetamol acts only on prostaglandin production in the brain.	Most take from 30 to 60 minutes to start working if taken as tablets or capsules. Intravenous or injected liquids are much faster. Most opioids are injected. Drips can maintain the concentration of the drug in the body, whereas tablets tend to peak and then decline in effect before the next dose can be taken. Sprays, creams or gels that can be absorbed through the skin are applied to treat muscle or joint pain. Sometimes patient controlled analgesia (PCA) is used - a button controlled device pumps analgesic intravenously, when needed. The amount that can be taken is regulated.

ANTI-INFLAMMATORIES

examples	uses	action	formulation/route
Aspirin and some non-opioids known as non-steroidal anti-inflammatory drugs (NSAIDS) e.g. ibuprofen	Reduce swelling and inflammation.	Prevent prostaglandin production - see analgesics above. (Note that paracetamol is not an anti-inflammatory).	See analgesics above.

Uses of drugs continued ...

ANTIBIOTICS

examples	uses	action	formulation/route
Penicillins e.g. ampicillin Tetracyclines e.g. doxycycline	Treatment of diseases and conditions caused by bacteria such as tuberculosis and abscesses.	Kill or prevent the growth of bacteria, e.g. • penicillins prevent cell wall development • tetracyclines interfere with protein synthesis. Many bacteria (like MRSA - methicillin resistant Staphylococcus aureus - and *Clostridium difficile*) are becoming resistant to most antibiotics.	Usually taken orally in capsule form, sometimes as a liquid. Given intravenously in more serious or deep-seated infections. May be administered topically as in eye drops or ointments.

ANTIHISTAMINES

examples	uses	action	formulation/route
Acrivastine	To treat and prevent allergic reactions such as the itching, sneezing and production of watery mucus found in hay fever.	Stops the effect of the chemical histamine produced by the immune system. It blocks the receptors that histamine stimulates. These receptors are found in many tissues, especially the nose, skin and eyes. Histamine increases blood flow and causes swelling through fluid loss from capillaries. It causes increased mucus production and itching. As it does not enter the brain, acrivastine is a *non-drowsy* anti-histamine.	Acrivastine and similar drugs are usually taken orally in tablet or capsule form, sometimes as a liquid. Antihistamines can be given intravenously in more serious cases of allergic shock, e.g. to wasp stings. Can also be used as a topical ointment or cream, e.g. to treat insect bites.

Uses of drugs continued ...

ANTIDEPRESSANTS

examples	uses	action	formulation/route
Three main types: Selective serotonin re-uptake inhibitors (SSRIs) e.g. Paroxetine hydrochloride Tricyclics (TCAs) e.g. clomipramine Monoamine oxidase inhibitors (MAOIs) e.g. Phenelzine	To alleviate depression e.g. feelings of despair or apathy, anxiety or panic attacks.	Depression is thought to be caused by a lack of chemical transmitters at nerve endings in the brain. In depression, brain cells are under--stimulated because there are too few transmitter molecules. Tricyclics block the reabsorption of transmitters. SSRIs block reabsorption of just the transmitter serotonin. MAOIs block the enzymes that break down the transmitters. Higher transmitter levels keep the brain cells stimulated.	Usually given as tablets or capsules, but clomipramine may be injected in severe illness.

CHEMICAL REPLACEMENTS

examples	uses	action	formulation/route
Insulin	For the treatment of type 1 diabetes when the pancreas produces insufficient insulin.	Directly replaces natural insulin. Insulin converts excess glucose in the blood into glycogen for storage in the liver and muscles. It restores the normal blood sugar balance.	Usually injected using a syringe or injection pen. As insulin is a protein, it is digested if taken orally. Insulin pump therapy allows insulin to flow at a controlled rate into the blood through a needle at the end of a tube. An insulin jet system forces insulin through a nozzle at high speed, so that it passes through the skin.

Uses of drugs continued ...

CYTOLOGICAL (CHEMOTHERAPY)

examples	uses	action	formulation/route
Cisplatin Tamoxifen	To kill cancer cells by stopping them from growing or dividing.	Interfere with the cell reproduction process. They are designed to have a greater effect on cancer cells than normal body cells, as cancers divide rapidly out of control. Cisplatin damages DNA to prevent cell growth and division. Tamoxifen opposes the effect of oestrogen, which stimulates some breast cancers.	Usually delivered intravenously, e.g. cysplatin is injected. A drip or portable pumping device can be used for some drugs. Tamoxifen and some others are given as tablets or capsules.

STIMULANTS

examples	uses	action	formulation/route
Amphetamines e.g. dexamphetamine Caffeine Respiratory e.g. Theophylline	To increase wakefulness, e.g. in narcolepsy, where people fall asleep during the day for no apparent reason. Some stimulants can help difficulty in breathing, e.g. in very young babies.	Increase activity in the parts of the brain which control wakefulness. They stimulate the release of noradrenaline by brain cells. Breathing stimulants act on the respiratory centre of the brain.	May be taken as tablets, capsules or by injection.

Uses of drugs continued ...

SEDATIVES

examples	uses	action	formulation/route
Temazepam	Treatment of persistent sleeplessness e.g. due to anxiety or pain.	Slow down brain activity by interfering with chemical activity in the brain to reduce communication between brain cells.	Usually taken as tablets, capsules or liquid.

HEART DRUGS

examples	uses	action	formulation/route
Digitalis drugs e.g. digoxin	To treat irregular, too rapid or weak heart beat e.g. following a heart attack.	Slow down the speed of heart beat by reducing the flow of electrical impulses through heart muscle. Strengthen heart beat by making the muscle contract more powerfully.	Digoxin and atenolol may be taken orally as tablets or a liquid. They may also be injected.
Beta blockers e.g. Atenolol	To treat angina - chest pain caused by too little oxygen reaching the heart muscle.	Adrenaline (the emergency or *fight or flight* hormone) acts on heart muscle at beta receptors. Blocking beta receptors in heart muscle reduces the speed and force of the heart beat, so less oxygen is needed.	
ACE inhibitors e.g. Captopril	To treat high blood pressure and angina.	Block the action of an enzyme that causes the constriction of blood vessels.	Captopril is given in tablets.
Statins	To treat or prevent heart disease.	Reduces cholesterol in the blood. They block an enzyme responsible for cholesterol production in the liver.	Statins come as tablets or capsules.

THERAPEUTIC TECHNIQUES

Physical techniques

Therapeutic drugs may be used in many cases of chemical imbalance in the body or to combat invading organisms. Many other causes of ill health that can't be treated by drug therapy or by drugs alone. There's a wide variety of physical techniques which will alleviate or cure them.

Such techniques include:

- surgery
- replacement surgery
- radiotherapy
- laser therapy
- physiotherapy, osteopathy and chiropractics
- acupuncture and other alternative therapies
- preventive therapies
- vaccination
- organ transplants
- blood and plasma transfusion.

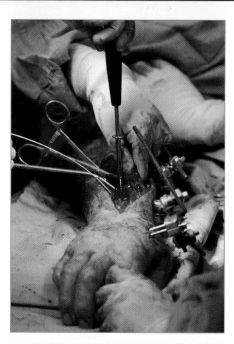

Surgery

The benefits of surgery have been recognised for many centuries, long before Western medicine. There's evidence from Ancient Egypt. Sushrata (600 BC) in Northern India wrote the world's oldest known surgical text, detailing many techniques, including plastic surgery.

Abulcasis, the great 10th century Arab surgeon, is often said to be the '*father of surgery*'.

Modern surgical techniques can be used to remove diseased tissue and repair or replace damaged or malfunctioning structures. Life threatening or painful conditions, from cancerous tumours and deep-seated abscesses to damaged knee cartilages, can be treated. Failed joints or eye lenses can be replaced. In cosmetic surgery, appearances may be improved.

Replacement surgery

Joint replacement surgery is highly effective for removing joint pain, correcting deformity and restoring movement, for example in advanced arthritis.

Other structures can also be replaced, but all must be strong enough to resist wear and be compatible with the body's defence systems.

Physiotherapy, osteopathy and chiropractics

These three offer different approaches to the treatment of the human movement systems - muscles, joints and skeleton. They all view human movement as central to health and well-being. Physical problems may be caused by illness, accident or ageing.

Physiotherapy lies within mainstream conventional medicine. Skills used by physiotherapists include manipulation therapy and therapeutic exercise. Physiotherapists also have an understanding of psychological, cultural and social factors which influence their clients.

Chiropractors believe that improper alignment of the vertebrae and the spinal cord causes ill-health by affecting the whole nervous system. Chiropractors use pressure to allow the vertebrae in the spinal column to realign themselves. They are also *whole body healers* who take into consideration other factors such as nutrition, stress management and so on.

Osteopaths also use manipulative techniques but put equal emphasis on the spine, joints, muscles, tendons and ligaments. They tend to use less force than chiropractors.

Chiropractics and osteopathy are considered to be *alternative medicine*, outside the mainstream. Both are accepted by many conventional medical practitioners, but evidence for their effectiveness is unclear.

Radiotherapy

Radiotherapy uses radiation, such as X-rays or gamma-rays, for the treatment of localised cancers and, occasionally, other diseases.

It's often used following surgery to destroy any remaining cancer cells. The radiation damages DNA. Normal cells, unlike cancer cells, can usually recover. Measured doses of radiation are used to destroy tumour cells with the minimum damage to the surrounding tissues.

A machine directs a beam of radiation into a cancer. Sometimes a solid radioactive material is placed close to, or inside, a tumour. Radioactive liquids are also used.

Laser therapy

Lasers can deliver highly accurate, high energy beams. They are used for a variety of microsurgical techniques, including the removal of birthmarks and the treatment of eye defects. In short sight, the lens system of the eye is too powerful. Laser surgery slightly flattens the centre of the cornea.

Vaccination

Vaccinations effectively teach the body how to make antibodies to destroy disease-causing organisms (pathogens).

Each antibody matches a specific antigen found on the pathogen. The vaccine contains antigens from weakened or dead bacteria or viruses. These stimulate an immune response and, after a short time, the correct antibodies are made and the memory of how to make the antibodies remains. If the real pathogen later appears in the body, a much faster response releases antibodies to rapidly destroy it before it can cause harm. You're immune to that disease.

Preventive therapies

A great many techniques can prevent or slow down the onset of disease.

For example, regular exercise with energy expenditure of about 4200 kJ per week (equivalent to walking for one hour, five days a week) gives significant health benefits. The fitness of the heart, blood vessels, muscles, bones and joints are all improved.

Acupuncture

Acupuncture is a branch of traditional Chinese medicine that's been practised for thousands of years. It's a very popular and well-established form of alternative medicine, used to treat pain and promote general health. It can help overcome addictions such as smoking and alcoholism. Ultra-fine metal needles are inserted at carefully selected points on the skin, according to the condition being treated.

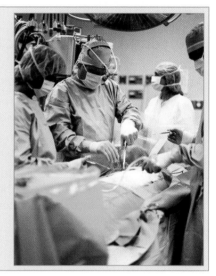

Organ transplants

Organs removed from donors replace damaged or failing organs, such as a kidney. Antigens may stimulate the body's immune response. So, relatives are used as donors whenever possible. Compatibility tests are carried out. In some cases tissues may be transplanted from within the same person, for example skin grafts or storage of blood prior to surgery.

Occasionally tissues from other species can be used, e.g. pig heart valves can be transplanted very successfully.

Blood transfusions

Blood transfusions are often life saving, e.g. if there has been massive blood loss in an accident or surgery, or in severe anaemia such as in sickle cell disease.

Crossmatching is important, as antigens in donated blood can stimulate an immune response and kill the recipient.

For example, group A individuals have the A antigen but B antibodies in their blood. Therefore they cannot be given goup B or group AB blood, which contain non-compatible antigen B. They can be given group O blood, which has no A or B antigens

In an emergency, or when cross-checked blood is not immediately available, plasma can be given. This increases the volume of blood and maintains the circulation. Plasma will not stimulate the immune reaction which sticks donated red cells together.

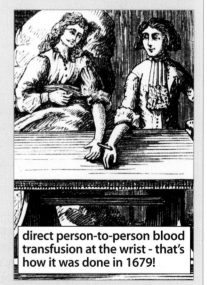

direct person-to-person blood transfusion at the wrist - that's how it was done in 1679!

Religious, cultural and individual beliefs

According to the Jehovah's Witnesses, the Bible prohibits the consumption, storage and tranfusion of blood, even in a life-saving emergency. This is just one example of cases when beliefs conflict with mainstream medical practice. Pro-life groups include people who actively resist euthanasia, human cloning, human embryonic stem cell research, abortion and certain types of birth control. They believe that human life should be valued from fertilisation to natural death.

NEW DRUGS

How new therapeutic drugs are developed

On average it takes 10 to 12 years and £550 million to develop a new drug.

Every new drug has to go through the rigorous and expensive processes of selection and testing before it can be sold as a safe and effective product.

In the UK, pharmaceutical companies spend about £10 million pounds every day on developing new drugs

One quarter of the top 100 drugs are British discoveries.

Selection and pre-clinical trials

Initial research in the laboratory produces new compounds that are screened for their likely action as drugs.

Chemists used to make about 100 new compounds every year. Now, robotic techniques can produce *half a million* new compounds *every week*.

Screening is carried out by targeting possible uses. Computer techniques allow a million compounds to be screened in a few weeks.

A variety of techniques, including tests on tissue cultures, help in selecting the most promising compounds. Those compounds are sent for animal testing. Computer modelling and test tube investigations cannot predict all the effects of the compound.

Clinical trials

Phase 1

The drug is tested on a small number of human volunteers. Dose limits and formulation (tablet, capsule or injection) are established.

Phase 2

A large number of patients with the condition to be treated are given the medicine - to test that it works and does not have unacceptable side effects. Phase 1 and Phase 2 are sometimes combined.

Phase 3

The drug is tested on a large number (typically several thousand) of patients given a full course of treatment. It is compared with other drugs and/or a placebo (dummy drug). If successful, i.e. safe and effective, the drug data is presented to the authorities for approval. If approved, a marketing authority is issued.

Phase 4

The newly licensed drug is studied in large numbers of patients to check its effectiveness and safety in general.

Manufacturing the new drug

Initially, only small quantities of the new drug have to be made.

Then enough has to be made for the clinical trials, increasing for Phase 3.

By Phase 4 the manufacture has to move to large scale production. Marketing becomes an important factor.

Chemical engineers are responsible for the scaling up process when changing from laboratory to high volume production.

Enough of the new drug must be sold as quickly as possible to cover the development costs and fund future developments.

For prescription drugs, marketing is directed at the medical professionals who will authorise and prescribe the drug.

It's important that the drug is shown to be more effective than any existing drugs, both in its action and value for money.

Not *all* existing treatments are available to *all* people

In November 2006 news broke that Fraser, the son of Gordon Brown (then Chancellor of the Exchequer) had cystic fibrosis.

At that time, under the NHS, only certain areas of the UK automatically tested newborn children for the condition. Treatments and tests vary in availability, according to priorities set by the health service.

For many reasons, there are regional variations in the treatments that patients can receive and the lengths of waiting lists.

Risk factors

Most treatments have **side effects**.

The *benefits* of treatment have to be weighed up against the potential *risks*.

In some cases, the risk that the patient will die or be severely handicapped as a result of treatment is high. For example, an old person may not be fit enough to undertake a major operation under a general anaesthetic.

Sometimes, treatments are not given to patients because their quality of life may be badly affected.

In other cases, a patient may be allergic to a drug or risk becoming addicted if long term use is necessary. For example, opioids (narcotic drugs) used for long term pain relief carry the risk of addiction.

Personal factors

Religious, cultural or personal values and beliefs can affect which treatments are acceptable to people.

For example pro-life groups believe that human life starts at fertilisation. So, abortion for *any* reason is not acceptable.

Jehovah's Witnesses believe that blood transfusions act against the word of the Bible. (See *Using therapeutic techniques*).

pro-life marchers in America at the *March for Life* in 2002
credit: http://transporter.com/apologia/life/

Financial factors

In the UK, the watchdog on medicines is the National Institute for Clinical Excellence (NICE). It was set up to promote the cost--effective use of drugs by the NHS.

NICE is responsible for approving drugs for use in the UK. They take risk factors (see *Risk factors*) and financial factors into account.

NHS Trusts protested when NICE approved the use of the breast cancer drug Herceptin because the cost is about £20 000 per woman for a year's treatment. They were worried that they would have to cut other treatments to pay for it.

Newbury and Community Primary Care Trust appealed against the decision on the grounds that Herceptin was unaffordable and too many other patients would suffer. They lost the appeal.

Each hospital trust has a limited amount of money to spend. So, sometimes, hard decisions have to be made about which treatments can be given and who will be able to receive them. From time to time, decisions are challenged in court.

Some people *go private*. If they have enough money (or insurance), they pay for private treatment to avoid waiting lists or in the hope of better treatment.

Ethical factors

Ethics enter into any decision where a value judgement or moral decision has to be made.

The question is:

'Is this the right decision under the circumstances'

The potential benefit to the patient has to be taken into account.

Difficult decisions can include:

'Should we switch off the life support machine?'

'Should I choose pregnancy, abortion or adoption?'